Glencoe
CHEMISTRY
MATTER AND CHANGE

Section Focus
Transparency
Masters

D1457153

Glencoe
McGraw-Hill

New York, New York   Columbus, Ohio   Woodland Hills, California   Peoria, Illinois

Glencoe
CHEMISTRY
MATTER AND CHANGE

Hands-On Learning:
Laboratory Manual, SE/TE
Forensics Laboratory Manual, SE/TE
CBL Laboratory Manual, SE/TE
Small-Scale Laboratory Manual, SE/TE
ChemLab and MiniLab Worksheets

Review/Reinforcement:
Study Guide for Content Mastery, SE/TE
Solving Problems: A Chemistry Handbook
Reviewing Chemistry
Guided Reading Audio Program

Applications and Enrichment:
Challenge Problems
Supplemental Problems

Assessment:
Chapter Assessment
MindJogger Videoquizzes (VHS/DVD)
TestCheck Software, Windows/MacIntosh

Teacher Resources:
Lesson Plans
Block Scheduling Lesson Plans
Spanish Resources
Section Focus Transparencies and Masters
Math Skills Transparencies and Masters
Teaching Transparencies and Masters
Solutions Manual

Technology:
Chemistry Interactive CD-ROM
Vocabulary PuzzleMaker Software,
Windows/MacIntosh
Glencoe Science Web site:
science.glencoe.com

Send all inquiries to:
Glencoe/McGraw-Hill
8787 Orion Place
Columbus, OH 43240-4027

ISBN 0-07-824546-X
Printed in the United States of America.
2 3 4 5 6 7 8 9 10 047 09 08 07 06 05 04 03

Contents

To the Teacher

A Section Focus Transparency is provided for every section in the Student Edition of *Chemistry: Matter and Change.* Each transparency contains two questions related to the transparency image. In addition, each transparency is reproduced as a master in this booklet. Teaching strategies and possible answers to the questions for each transparency can be found at the back of this booklet.

Purpose

A Section Focus Transparency provides a common jumping off point as students begin a new section in their text. The thought-provoking questions encourage students to use prior knowledge and their own experiences as they begin to build a context for the section material. These transparencies invite all students to participate, stressing exploration and discussion rather than "right" answers.

Uses

▶ Have the transparency projected before students enter class. It will help focus their attention and maximize classroom time by giving them something to start thinking about.

▶ The transparency masters may make it easier for students to view the images and discuss the questions. You might suggest that students write notes on the masters and keep them in their chemistry folders as a study tool.

▶ You might use the master as a baseline assessment tool. It will help both you and your students assess prior knowledge before beginning a new section.

▶ Revisit the transparency at the end of the section to assess students' new understandings. Discuss again the questions on the transparency. What new information can students bring to the discussion that they couldn't before?

▶ Employ the teaching suggestions provided in the Teacher Guide beginning on page T106. They provide helpful strategies for using the master as a teaching tool.

SECTION FOCUS TRANSPARENCY MASTER

Protection from the Sun

Use with Chapter 1,
Section 1.1

❶ How are these people protecting themselves from the Sun?

❷ Why is this protection necessary?

SECTION FOCUS TRANSPARENCY MASTER   ②

Weight and Mass

**Use with Chapter 1,
Section 1.2**

❶ Do you think this astronaut weighs more, less, or the same on the Moon as he weighs on Earth?

❷ Do you think this astronaut's mass is more, less, or the same on the Moon as it is on Earth?

SECTION FOCUS TRANSPARENCY MASTER   **3**

What's killing the plants?

**Use with Chapter 1,
Section 1.3**

❶   What is wrong with this plant?

❷   How could you find out what is harming the plant?

SECTION FOCUS TRANSPARENCY MASTER

Scientific Research

**Use with Chapter 1,
Section 1.4**

❶ What research might this scientist be doing?

❷ What practical application might there be to this
research?

SECTION FOCUS TRANSPARENCY MASTER **5**

SI Units

Use with Chapter 2, Section 2.1

EVENT: Long Jump

E. Johnson	6.90 m
J. Faklaris	7.15 m
M. Gillespie	6.83 m
R. Harris	7.05 m
G. Leblanc	6.95 m

❶ Who won?

❷ Compare the distances jumped with the length of a common object.

How much is it?

**Use with Chapter 2,
Section 2.2**

❶ How many dimes are in $5?

❷ How many quarters are in $20?

Name _____ Date _____ Class _____

Who is the better player?

**Use with Chapter 2,
Section 2.3**

❶ Which player won this round?

❷ Which player has the better—more accurate—throw?

Representing Data

Use with Chapter 2, Section 2.4

Day of Week	Amount of Rain (cm)
Monday	2.2
Tuesday	0.1
Wednesday	0.7
Thursday	1.5
Friday	0.0
Saturday	0.0
Sunday	3.1

❶ Based on the data given, which day received the most rain?

❷ How might this data be better organized?

SECTION FOCUS TRANSPARENCY MASTER ⑨

States of Matter

❶   What matter is shown in all three photographs?

❷   What is different about the matter in each photograph?

SECTION FOCUS TRANSPARENCY MASTER

10

Physical and Chemical Changes

Use with Chapter 3, Section 3.2

❶ How is the tree changed by each action shown?

❷ Which action do you think shows a more complete change?

SECTION FOCUS TRANSPARENCY MASTER

Mixtures

❶ How is the substance in photograph B made?

❷ What does it have in common with the substance in photograph A? Photograph C?

SECTION FOCUS TRANSPARENCY MASTER **12**

Common Elements and Compounds

Use with Chapter 3,
Section 3.4

Abundance of Elements in Earth's Crust

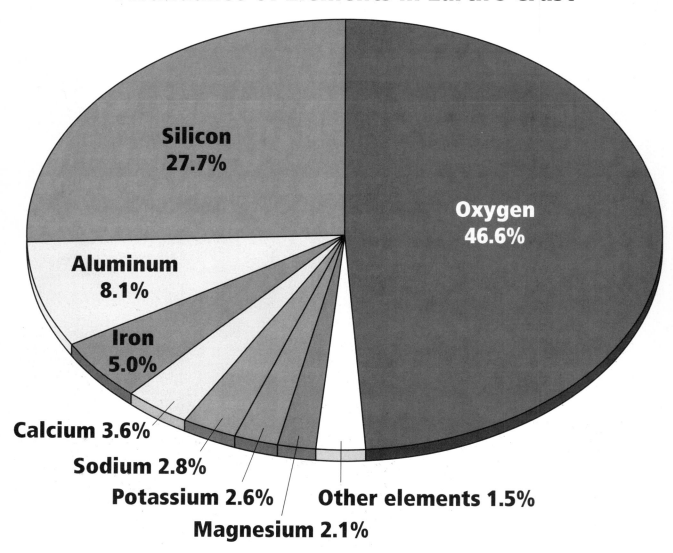

Silicon
27.7%

Oxygen
46.6%

Aluminum
8.1%

Iron
5.0%

Calcium 3.6%

Sodium 2.8%

Potassium 2.6%

Magnesium 2.1%

Other elements 1.5%

❶ Which element is the most abundant in Earth's crust?

❷ What are some common items that are made up of some
of these elements?

SECTION FOCUS TRANSPARENCY MASTER   **13**

Gold Atoms

**Use with Chapter 4,
Section 4.1**

❶ Does the gold dust have the same properties as the gold
bars? Explain.

❷ Is there a point at which gold can be broken into particles
so small that the particles do not retain the properties of
gold?

Models of an Atom

**Use with Chapter 4,
Section 4.2**

❶ What physical characteristics do these two models of an atom have in common?

❷ How do the two models differ?

SECTION FOCUS TRANSPARENCY MASTER **15**

Atoms and Elements

**Use with Chapter 4,
Section 4.3**

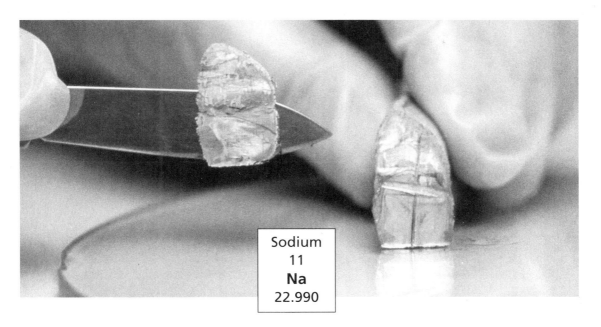

Sodium
11
Na
22.990

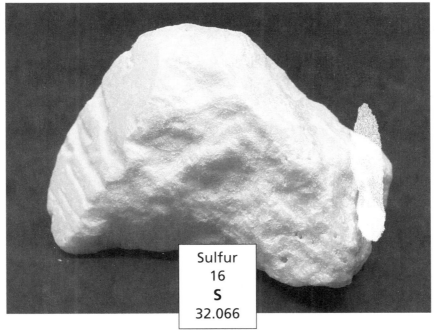

Sulfur
16
S
32.066

❶ How do these two elements differ in their properties?

❷ How might the atoms of these two elements differ?

Radiation

❶ What does this symbol mean?

❷ What should you do when you see this symbol?

SECTION FOCUS TRANSPARENCY MASTER   **17**

Light Waves

Use with Chapter 5,
Section 5.1

❶   What makes the colors in a rainbow?

❷   What other types of waves exist?

SECTION FOCUS TRANSPARENCY MASTER

Atomic Orbitals

**Use with Chapter 5,
Section 5.2**

❶ Does it take more energy for the painter to climb to the middle rung of the ladder or to the top rung of the ladder?

❷ Suppose the painter dropped his paintbrush from the top rung of the ladder. Later, the painter dropped the same paintbrush from the middle rung of the ladder. From which level did the paintbrush hit the ground with more energy?

SECTION FOCUS TRANSPARENCY MASTER (19)

Electron Configurations

Use with Chapter 5, Section 5.3

❶ Which seats in the arena are likely to be in more demand?

❷ Imagine that center court represents an atom's nucleus.
Which part of the arena represents energy levels? Which
part represents individual orbitals?

SECTION FOCUS TRANSPARENCY MASTER **20**

Classification

**Use with Chapter 6,
Section 6.1**

❶ How are most library books classified?

❷ Why is such a classification system useful?

SECTION FOCUS TRANSPARENCY MASTER **21**

Cycles

**Use with Chapter 6,
Section 6.2**

❶ What cycle do the photographs illustrate?

❷ What should the missing photograph in the cycle show?
How do you know this?

SECTION FOCUS TRANSPARENCY MASTER

Inferring Characteristics

**Use with Chapter 6,
Section 6.3**

❶ What clues does the arrangement of the football players on the field give about the functions of their positions?

❷ What characteristics does a football player have based on the position played?

SECTION FOCUS TRANSPARENCY MASTER **23**

s-Block Elements

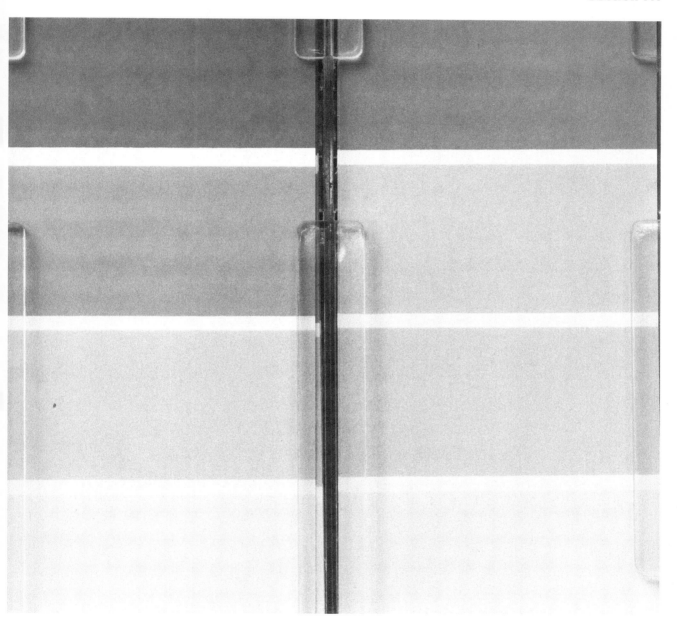

❶ How are these two strips of color similar? How are they different?

❷ Look at the elements in the first two columns in the periodic table, which are the s-block elements. What relationships might you expect to find among these elements?

SECTION FOCUS TRANSPARENCY MASTER

Noble Gases

Use with Chapter 7, Section 7.2

❶ What element is producing the red light? Where is this element located in the periodic table?

❷ Which elements in the periodic table are most similar to the element producing the light?

SECTION FOCUS TRANSPARENCY MASTER (25)

Transition Elements

Use with Chapter 7, Section 7.3

❶ Why do you think gold and silver were used to make these ancient coins?

❷ What are some other uses for these elements?

SECTION FOCUS TRANSPARENCY MASTER

Formation of Ions

**Use with Chapter 8,
Section 8.1**

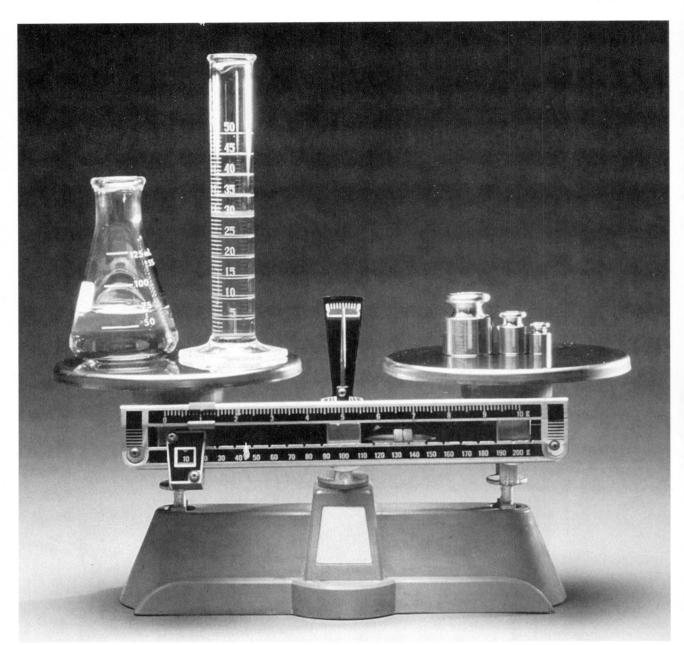

❶ How are the masses on this balance similar to the
numbers of electrons and protons in an atom?

❷ What would happen to the balance if mass was added to
or removed from one of the pans?

SECTION FOCUS TRANSPARENCY MASTER
27

Forming Rust

**Use with Chapter 8,
Section 8.2**

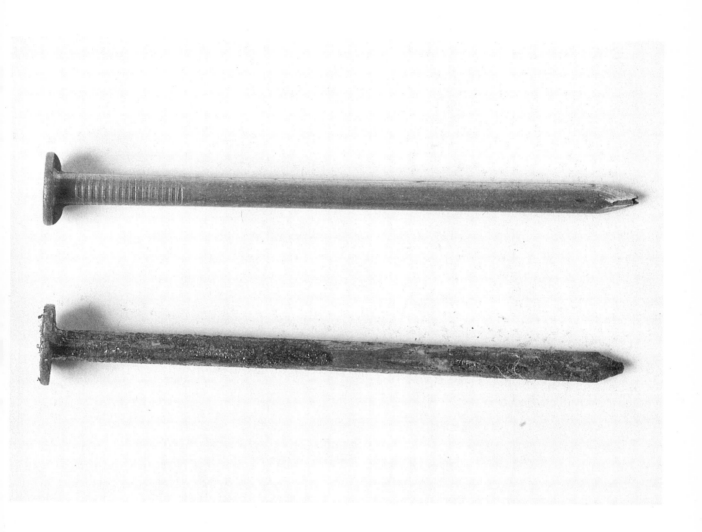

❶ How do the two iron nails differ in appearance and in their properties?

❷ What chemical reaction do you think caused the appearance of the nail on the bottom?

SECTION FOCUS TRANSPARENCY MASTER **28**

Combining Objects

Use with Chapter 8,
Section 8.3

❶ How many clothespins and how many articles of clothing
do you see in A? B? C? D?

❷ Use the symbols X, Y, and Z to construct formulas that
represent the relationship between the clothespins and
articles of clothing in A, B, C, and D. Define what the
symbols X, Y, and Z stand for in your formulas.

SECTION FOCUS TRANSPARENCY MASTER (29)

Properties of Metals

**Use with Chapter 8,
Section 8.4**

❶ Can you identify the metal in this photograph? How can
you tell that it is a metal?

❷ What is being done to the metal shown, and what does
that show about the properties of metals?

SECTION FOCUS TRANSPARENCY MASTER

A Special Kind of "Ice"

**Use with Chapter 9,
Section 9.1**

Oxygen   Carbon   Oxygen

❶ What is the common name for the special "ice" shown, and what is it often used for?

❷ How does the ball-and-stick model of this substance show that it is different from ordinary ice?

SECTION FOCUS TRANSPARENCY MASTER **31**

What's in a name?

**Use with Chapter 9,
Section 9.2**

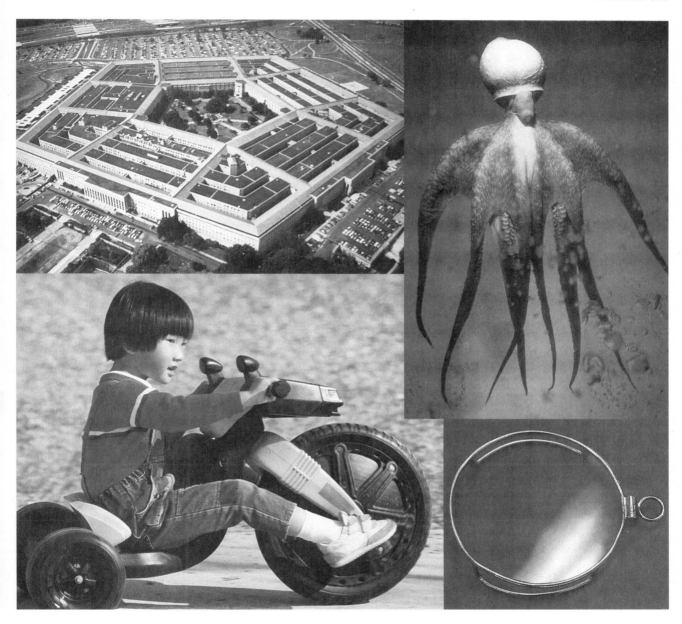

❶ What objects can you identify in the pictures?

❷ What information do the first few letters of the names of
the objects reveal?

SECTION FOCUS TRANSPARENCY MASTER

32

Combining Units

**Use with Chapter 9,
Section 9.3**

❶ What are the small construction-set units being used for?

❷ How are the small units able to be used in this way?

SECTION FOCUS TRANSPARENCY MASTER (33)

Taking Up Space

**Use with Chapter 9,
Section 9.4**

❶ What is shown in the picture?

❷ Describe the geometrical shape of each arrangement, and explain why, in general, these shapes take form.

SECTION FOCUS TRANSPARENCY MASTER

34

Tug-of-War

**Use with Chapter 9,
Section 9.5**

❶ What is happening in the picture?

❷ Do you think the rope will be "shared" equally by the end of the contest? Why or why not?

SECTION FOCUS TRANSPARENCY MASTER 35

Evidence of Chemical Change

**Use with Chapter 10,
Section 10.1**

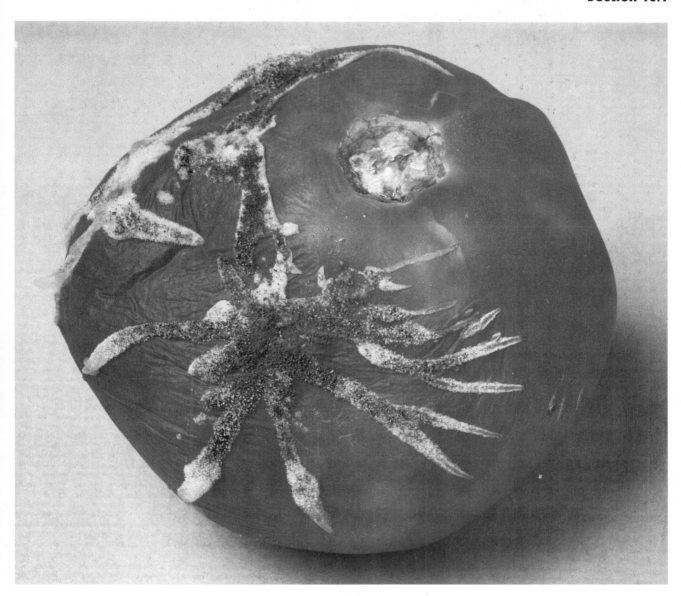

❶ Describe the changes in appearance and odor that
this food has undergone. Can any of these changes be
reversed?

❷ Has the identity of the materials that make up the food
changed?

SECTION FOCUS TRANSPARENCY MASTER 36

Types of Chemical Reactions

Use with Chapter 10, Section 10.2

❶ Describe the appearance of unreacted silver, copper, and iron metals.

❷ What do you think happened to the metals to make them look like the items pictured?

SECTION FOCUS TRANSPARENCY MASTER   37

Solid from Liquids

**Use with Chapter 10,
Section 10.3**

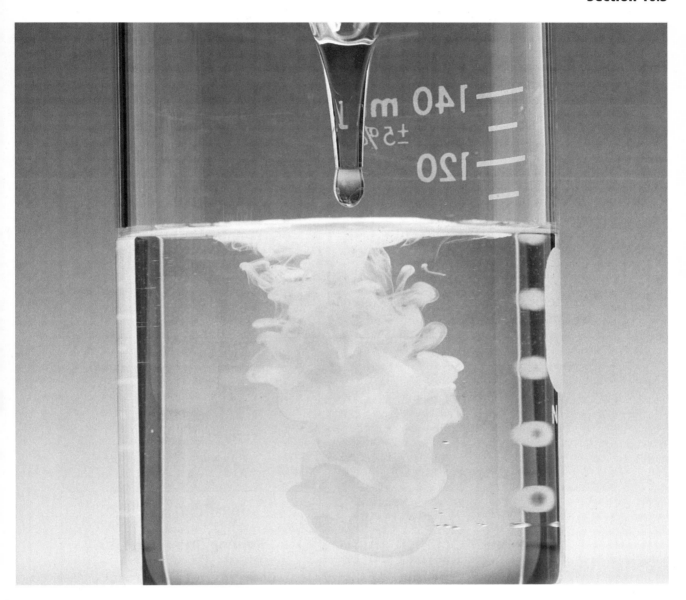

❶ As discussed in Section 10.2, what type of reaction forms a solid when two aqueous solutions are mixed?

❷ Why do you think it is necessary for the mixed compounds to be in aqueous solution in order for the reaction to occur?

SECTION FOCUS TRANSPARENCY MASTER   **38**

Comparing Counting Units

Use with Chapter 11,
Section 11.1

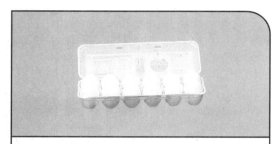

Mass (kg)	7×10^{-2}
Volume (m³)	5×10^{-5}
Counting Unit	dozen
Numerical Value of Counting Unit	12

Mass (kg)	7×10^{-1}
Volume (m³)	2×10^{-3}
Counting Unit	pair
Numerical Value of Counting Unit	2

Mass (kg)	5×10^{-3}
Volume (m³)	7×10^{-6}
Counting Unit	ream
Numerical Value of Counting Unit	500

Mass (kg)	7×10^{-3}
Volume (m³)	2×10^{-5}
Counting Unit	gross
Numerical Value of Counting Unit	144

❶ What happens to the numerical value of the counting unit as the size of the item that it counts decreases?

❷ How would you describe the numerical value of a counting unit that is needed to count atoms and molecules?

SECTION FOCUS TRANSPARENCY MASTER

Count Per Weight

**Use with Chapter 11,
Section 11.2**

❶ The shrimp pictured here are 10–12 count, that is, there are 10–12 shrimp per pound. How many shrimp would you get if you bought 3 pounds?

❷ What type of measurement is used to determine the cost of the shrimp?

SECTION FOCUS TRANSPARENCY MASTER (40)

Conservation of Mass

Use with Chapter 11, Section 11.3

❶ How would the mass of this assembled barbell compare with the mass of an unassembled barbell?

❷ How do you think the combined mass of one carbon-12 atom and two oxygen-16 atoms compares with the mass of a molecule of carbon dioxide?

SECTION FOCUS TRANSPARENCY MASTER

Percent Composition

Use with Chapter 11,
Section 11.4

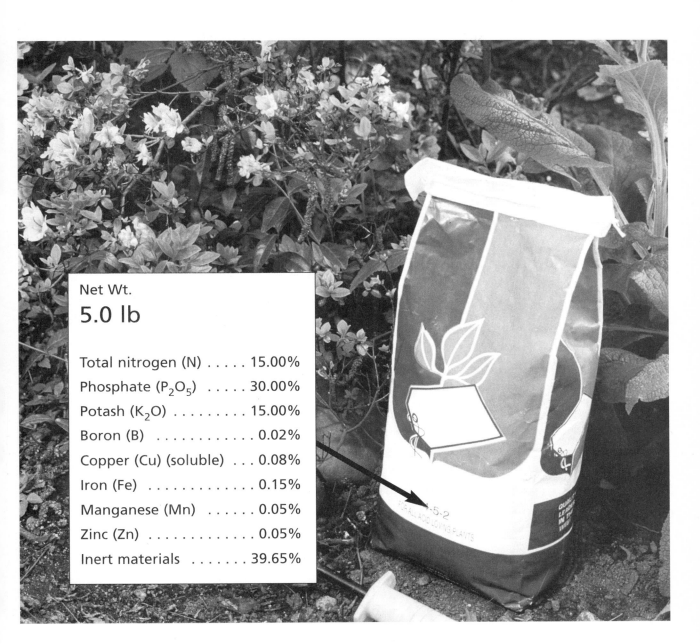

Net Wt.

5.0 lb

Total nitrogen (N) 15.00%

Phosphate (P_2O_5) 30.00%

Potash (K_2O) 15.00%

Boron (B) 0.02%

Copper (Cu) (soluble) . . . 0.08%

Iron (Fe) 0.15%

Manganese (Mn) 0.05%

Zinc (Zn) 0.05%

Inert materials 39.65%

❶ What is the total percentage of all the materials in the fertilizer except the inert materials? What two ways can you calculate this percentage?

❷ What is the weight of available phosphate in the fertilizer?

SECTION FOCUS TRANSPARENCY MASTER **42**

Soaking Up Water

Use with Chapter 11,
Section 11.5

❶ From where in the soaked sponge is the water coming?

❷ Some crystalline substances absorb water from the
atmosphere and remain solids. What characteristic of
the crystal structure might account for this property?

SECTION FOCUS TRANSPARENCY MASTER **43**

Balancing Reactions

**Use with Chapter 12,
Section 12.1**

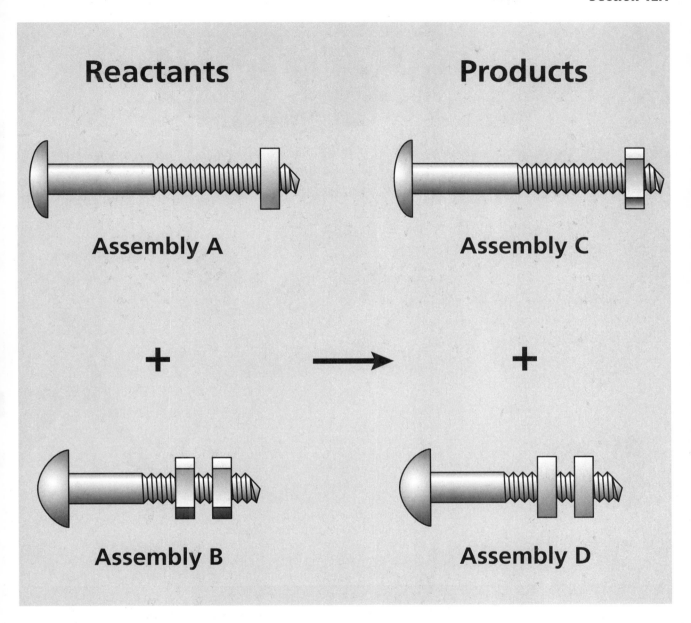

Reactants   **Products**

Assembly A   Assembly C

+   →   +

Assembly B   Assembly D

❶ Are there enough nuts and bolts in the assemblies on the left to make the assemblies on the right?

❷ What minimum number of each reactant nut-and-bolt assembly will you need to make the product assemblies shown without any nuts and bolts remaining? How many of each product assembly will be made from your answer?

Using the Right Amounts

**Use with Chapter 12,
Section 12.2**

Chocolate Chip Cookies

Makes 42 cookies

1/2 cup butter
1/2 cup brown sugar
1/2 cup granulated sugar
1 egg
1/2 teaspoon vanilla

1 cup sifted all-purpose flour
1/2 teaspoon salt
1/2 teaspoon baking soda
1/2 cup chopped walnuts
1/2 cup semisweet chocolate chips

1. Cream together the first three ingredients.
2. Beat in the egg and the vanilla.
3. Sift and stir in the flour, salt, and baking soda.
4. Stir in the walnuts and chocolate chips.
5. Drop teaspoonfuls of batter well apart onto greased baking sheets.
6. Place sheets in middle of preheated 375° oven. Bake for 10 minutes.

❶ What is the product of this recipe?

❷ How would you adjust the ingredients in the recipe to make seven dozen cookies?

SECTION FOCUS TRANSPARENCY MASTER (45)

Limiting Reactants

❶ For what purpose is a fire blanket used?

❷ How do you think a fire blanket affects the reactants in a combustion reaction?

SECTION FOCUS TRANSPARENCY MASTER

46

Determining Efficiency

**Use with Chapter 12,
Section 12.4**

❶ If the ballplayer had 23 hits after 90 times at bat, how would you determine the efficiency of her batting?

❷ How do you think the efficiency of a chemical reaction might be measured?

SECTION FOCUS TRANSPARENCY MASTER (47)

Changes in Air Pressure

**Use with Chapter 13,
Section 13.1**

❶ How will the air pressure change as the mountain climber continues up the mountain?

❷ Why does the air pressure change?

SECTION FOCUS TRANSPARENCY MASTER   **48**

Forces of Attraction

❶ What evidence is there that the force of attraction
between items of clothing removed from a dryer is
electrical in nature?

❷ What evidence is there that forces of attraction exist
between atoms and molecules?

SECTION FOCUS TRANSPARENCY MASTER   **49**

Behavior of Liquids

Use with Chapter 13, Section 13.3

❶ Why is it better to soak dirty dishes in hot water than in cold water?

❷ How do you think molecules of hot water are different from molecules of cold water?

SECTION FOCUS TRANSPARENCY MASTER **50**

Changes in States of Matter

**Use with Chapter 13,
Section 13.4**

❶ What evidence is there that water has changed from one
state to another state?

❷ What conditions would keep the situation shown in the
photograph the same indefinitely?

SECTION FOCUS TRANSPARENCY MASTER **51**

Hot Gases

**Use with Chapter 14,
Section 14.1**

❶ What is coming out of the tail of this rocket?

❷ How do the rocket fuels enable this rocket to blast off?

SECTION FOCUS TRANSPARENCY MASTER **52**

Getting Ready to Fly

**Use with Chapter 14,
Section 14.2**

❶   What is inside a hot-air balloon?

❷   How are hot-air balloons inflated?

SECTION FOCUS TRANSPARENCY MASTER (53)

Delivering Energy

Use with Chapter 14, Section 14.3

❶ How can propane gas be changed to a liquid?

❷ Why is propane transported as a liquid and not as a gas?

SECTION FOCUS TRANSPARENCY MASTER **54**

Making Bread

Use with Chapter 14,
Section 14.4

❶ When baking bread, why is it important to measure the correct amounts of specific ingredients?

❷ When making industrial products, such as large volumes of hydrogen peroxide, how do these industrial processes measure the needed amounts of reactants (or gases) on so large a scale?

SECTION FOCUS TRANSPARENCY MASTER **55**

Solutions

❶ What evidence is there that ocean water is a solution of a
solid in a liquid?

❷ What evidence, shown by plants and animals, proves that
ocean water is a solution of a gas in a liquid?

SECTION FOCUS TRANSPARENCY MASTER

Concentration

**Use with Chapter 15,
Section 15.2**

❶ Suppose you wanted to select your favorite-flavored jelly bean from the jar without looking at the jelly beans. On what would your chance of selecting your favorite jelly bean depend?

❷ How could you express that chance as a percent?

SECTION FOCUS TRANSPARENCY MASTER **57**

Properties of Solutions

Use with Chapter 15,
Section 15.3

❶ What evidence is there that these pellets can melt ice? What evidence is there that the aqueous solution containing the dissolved pellets does not freeze at 0°C?

❷ What can you conclude about the freezing point of the aqueous pellet solution and the freezing point of the pure solvent, water?

Name _____ Date _____ Class _____

Heterogeneous and Homogeneous Mixtures

Use with Chapter 15, Section 15.4

❶ Why should the pitcher of orange juice be stirred before pouring the orange juice into a glass?

❷ Why doesn't the pitcher of apple juice need to be stirred before pouring the juice into a glass?

SECTION FOCUS TRANSPARENCY MASTER ⬤ **59**

Heat

**Use with Chapter 16,
Section 16.1**

❶ What do you observe in the picture?

❷ Why do firefighters wear protective clothing?

Getting Warmer

**Use with Chapter 16,
Section 16.2**

❶ What kind of warning label do you see on the package?

❷ When a pie has been heated, why is the filling usually warmer than the crust?

SECTION FOCUS TRANSPARENCY MASTER 61

Change in Energy

❶ Why is the ice cream melting?

❷ Is the ice cream an exothermic or an endothermic system?

SECTION FOCUS TRANSPARENCY MASTER

Heat of Reaction

**Use with Chapter 16,
Section 16.4**

❶ How can you tell that this football player is producing heat?
    Where does this heat come from?

❷ How are the player's rate of heat production and his level of
    physical exertion related?

SECTION FOCUS TRANSPARENCY MASTER (63)

Increasing Disorder

**Use with Chapter 16,
Section 16.5**

❶ What has happened to the glass of milk?

❷ If the picture of the unbroken glass of milk represents an
orderly situation, what does the other picture represent?

Collisions

❶ Look at the positions of the vehicles and their damage.
    What can you conclude about the situation?

❷ Why do you think some of the vehicles are more damaged
    than others?

SECTION FOCUS TRANSPARENCY MASTER 　　**65**

Moving Particles

Use with Chapter 17,
Section 17.2

❶ The tea bags were placed in the two glasses at the same time. In which glass are the tea particles moving faster? How do you know?

❷ Why do you think the particles are moving faster?

SECTION FOCUS TRANSPARENCY MASTER

Concentration of Particles

**Use with Chapter 17,
Section 17.3**

❶ What will happen when the cue stick hits the cue ball?

❷ How might decreasing the number of balls on the table affect the outcome?

SECTION FOCUS TRANSPARENCY MASTER (67)

Following the Steps

Use with Chapter 17,
Section 17.4

❶ What is a recipe?

❷ What may happen if the people in the picture don't
follow the recipe correctly?

SECTION FOCUS TRANSPARENCY MASTER **68**

Equilibrium: A State of Dynamic Balance

Use with Chapter 18, Section 18.1

❶ How quickly does the man have to remove water from the boat to keep it from sinking any lower?

❷ What would happen if the man began removing water more quickly? More slowly?

SECTION FOCUS TRANSPARENCY MASTER **69**

Factors Affecting Chemical Equilibrium

Use with Chapter 18, Section 18.2

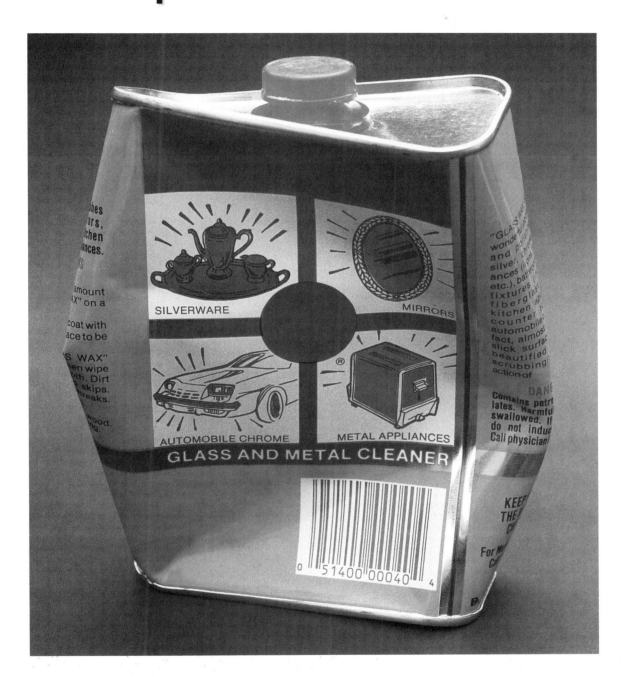

❶ How would you describe this can?

❷ How could this have happened?

SECTION FOCUS TRANSPARENCY MASTER **70**

Using Equilibrium Constants

**Use with Chapter 18,
Section 18.3**

❶ What has happened to the fudge from the first to the
second picture?

❷ What might you add to the fudge to make it harder?
What might you add to make it softer?

Section Focus Transparency Masters

SECTION FOCUS TRANSPARENCY MASTER 71

Properties of Acids and Bases

Use with Chapter 19,
Section 19.1

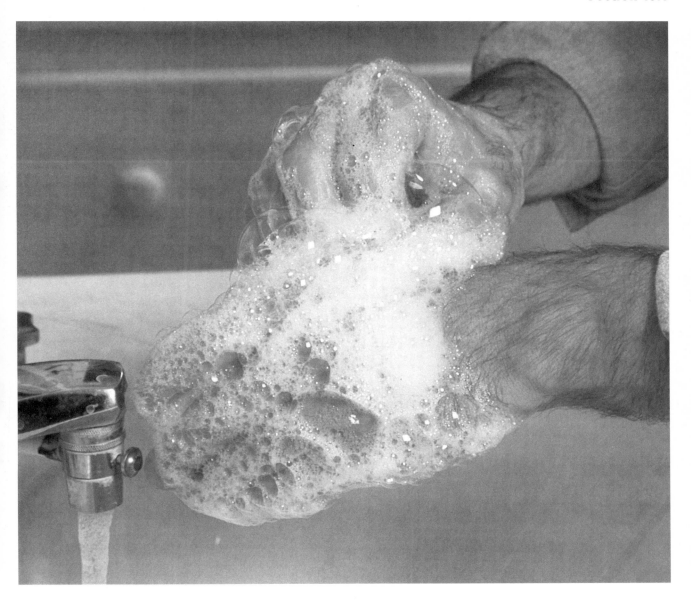

❶ What is one word that describes the feel of the bases used in soaps?

❷ Chapter 19 discusses both acids and bases. What terms come to mind when either acids or bases are mentioned?

Strengths of Acids

**Use with Chapter 19,
Section 19.2**

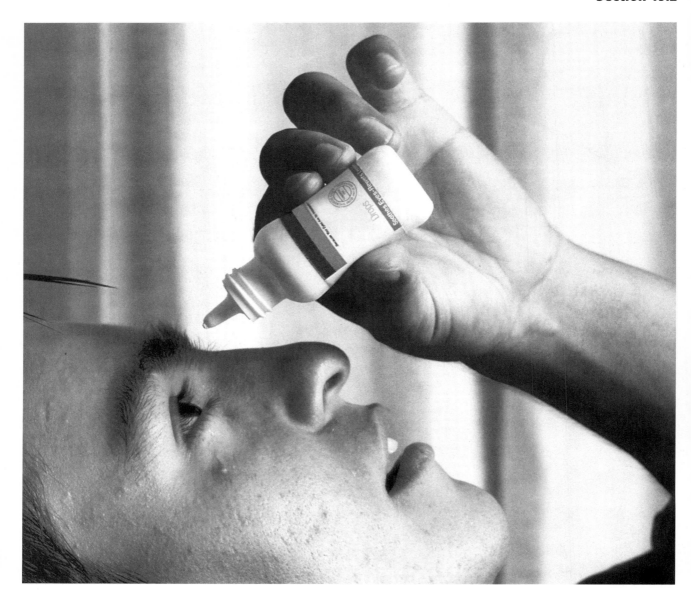

❶ Eyedrops frequently contain boric acid. Why do you think this acid can be dropped safely into an eye?

❷ What acids could not be used in eyedrops? Why?

Measuring Acidity

**Use with Chapter 19,
Section 19.3**

❶ Why do you think the swimming pool water is being tested?

❷ What might happen if the readings were not what they should be?

SECTION FOCUS TRANSPARENCY MASTER (74)

Neutralizing Soil

Use with Chapter 19,
Section 19.4

❶ Lime is added to soil that has a low pH to bring the pH
back to nearly neutral. Infer what type of compound
lime is.

❷ What do you think might happen to the soil if too much
lime is added?

SECTION FOCUS TRANSPARENCY MASTER   **75**

Bleaching

**Use with Chapter 20,
Section 20.1**

❶   How does the bleach affect the fabric?

❷   What causes this effect?

SECTION FOCUS TRANSPARENCY MASTER

Balancing Numbers

**Use with Chapter 20,
Section 20.2**

❶ If a person borrows money and pays some of it back, what effect does this payment have on the total amount owed?

❷ If the person borrows additional money, what effect does this additional loan have on the total amount owed?

SECTION FOCUS TRANSPARENCY MASTER

77

Giving and Taking

**Use with Chapter 20,
Section 20.3**

❶ How would you describe what is happening? Would you say that one runner is giving the baton or that the baton is being taken by the other runner?

❷ What other events involve both giving and taking?

Voltaic Cells

❶ What type of energy makes this car run?

❷ Where does this energy come from?

SECTION FOCUS TRANSPARENCY MASTER (79)

Corrosion

❶ What has caused the rusting of iron on this ship?

❷ What type of redox reaction is the iron undergoing?

SECTION FOCUS TRANSPARENCY MASTER

80

Electroplating

❶ Why are these steel auto parts being plated with chromium?

❷ Why do you think electricity must be supplied to make this
redox reaction occur?

Name _____ Date _____ Class _____

Organic and Inorganic Compounds

Use with Chapter 22, Section 22.1

❶ Which items in this photo do you think contain organic compounds, and which are entirely inorganic?

❷ What organic compound does this barbecue grill burn to produce heat?

SECTION FOCUS TRANSPARENCY MASTER **82**

Properties of Methane

**Use with Chapter 22,
Section 22.2**

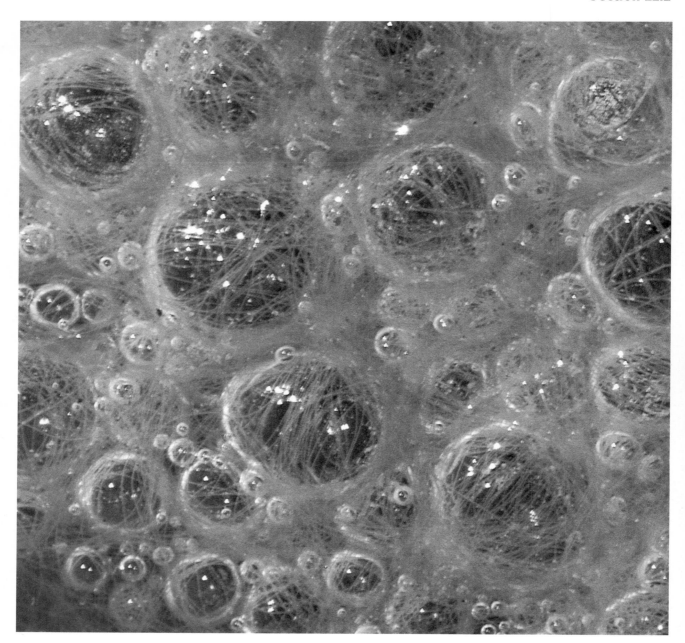

❶ This photo shows a close-up view of the bottom of a swamp. What clues suggest that the swamp is producing methane?

❷ On the basis of the photo, what can you conclude about the physical properties of methane?

Unsaturated Hydrocarbons

Use with Chapter 22, Section 22.3

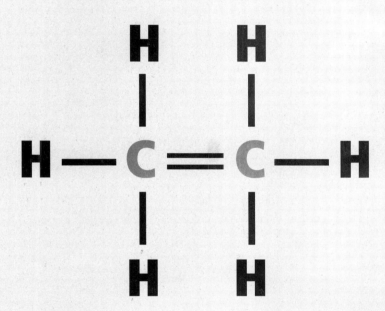

❶ What is wrong with this structure?

❷ Without changing the number of carbon atoms, how could you redraw the structure to make it correct?

SECTION FOCUS TRANSPARENCY MASTER   **84**

Optical Isomers

**Use with Chapter 22,
Section 22.4**

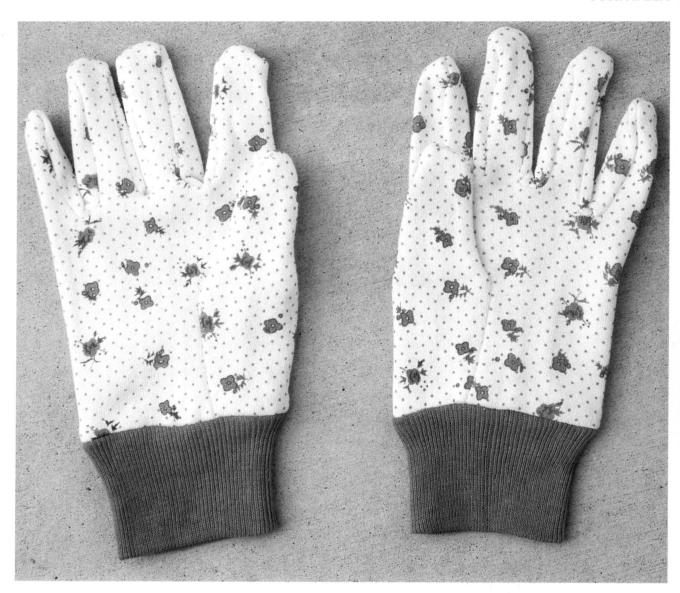

❶ How are these gloves similar, and how are they different?

❷ Can you rotate these gloves so they look the same?

SECTION FOCUS TRANSPARENCY MASTER **85**

Petroleum

**Use with Chapter 22,
Section 22.5**

❶ How do oil companies obtain petroleum?

❷ How is petroleum used?

SECTION FOCUS TRANSPARENCY MASTER **86**

A Source of Many Materials

**Use with Chapter 23,
Section 23.1**

❶ The briquettes in the central photograph are made of what element?

❷ The element you named is the source of many of the useful materials shown. What are the names of these materials?

Section Focus Transparency Masters

SECTION FOCUS TRANSPARENCY MASTER

A Useful Organic Liquid

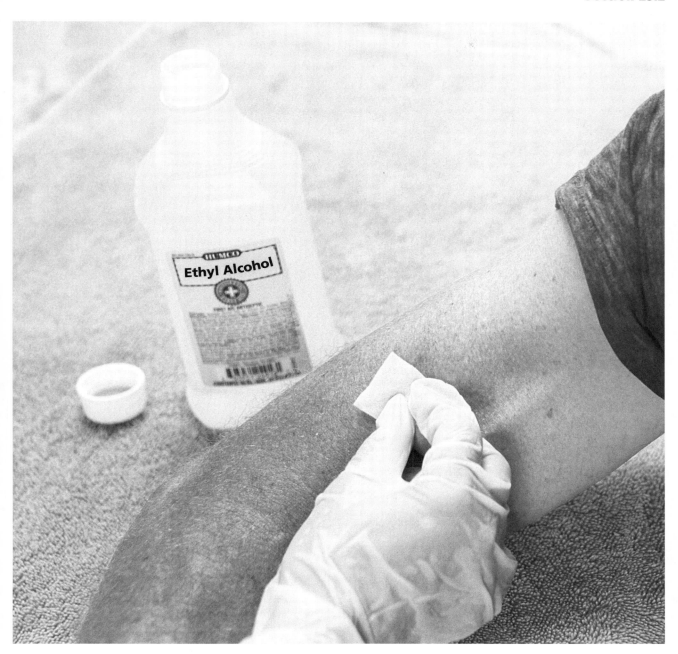

❶ For what purpose do you think this liquid is being used?

❷ List some properties of this liquid, and describe another of its uses.

SECTION FOCUS TRANSPARENCY MASTER

A Powerful Solvent

**Use with Chapter 23,
Section 23.3**

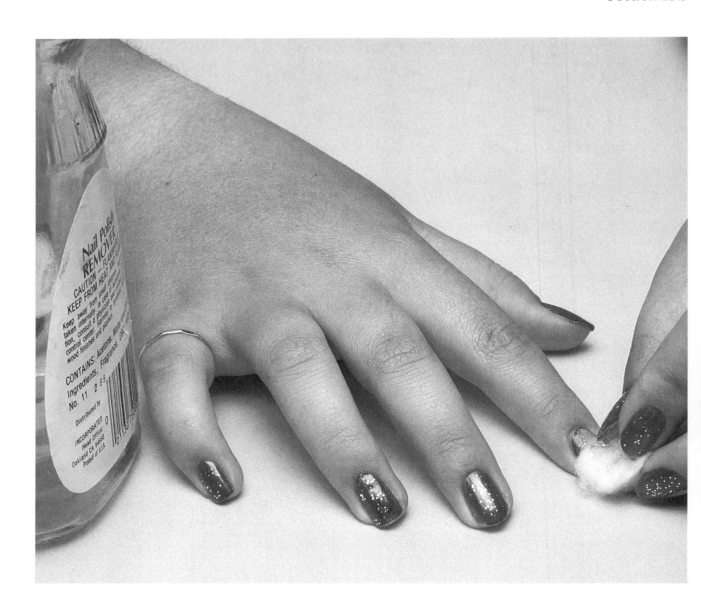

❶ How does nail polish remover take off the nail polish from fingernails?

❷ What property must nail polish remover have to be able to take off nail polish?

SECTION FOCUS TRANSPARENCY MASTER **89**

Saturated and Unsaturated Fats

Use with Chapter 23, Section 23.4

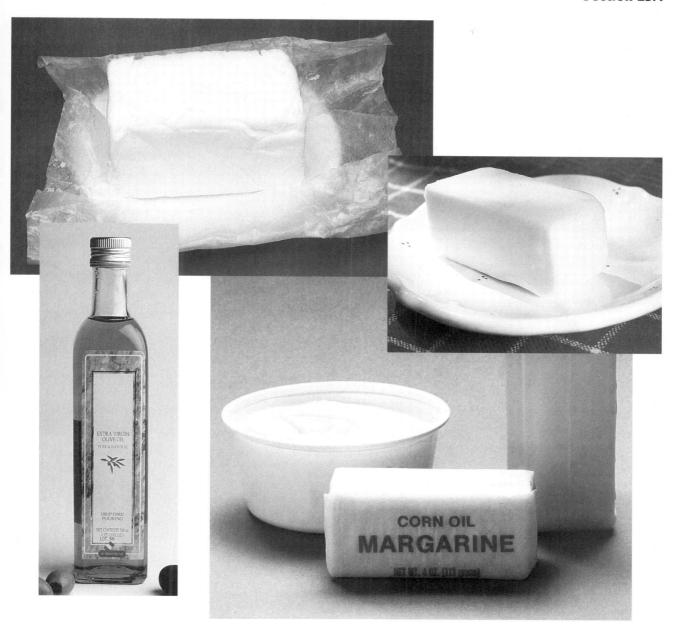

❶ Compare and contrast the fats shown.

❷ All the fats are at room temperature. How do their melting points vary?

SECTION FOCUS TRANSPARENCY MASTER **90**

Polymers

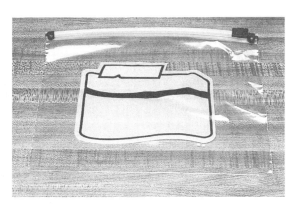

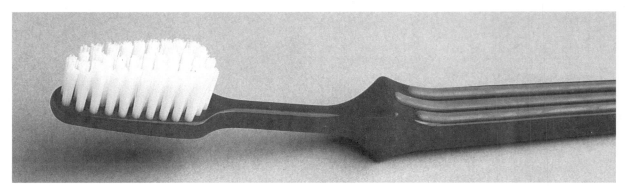

❶ What are all of the objects made of?

❷ How do the properties of the materials in these objects vary?

91

Protein Polymers

Nylon thread

Feather

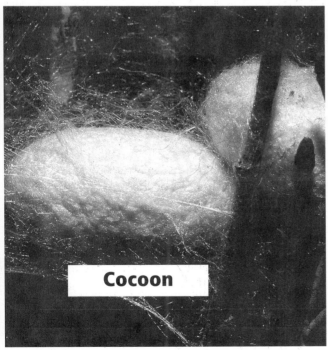

Cocoon

❶ What are the characteristics of the nylon thread?

❷ How does the nylon differ from the polymers that make up the cocoon and the feather?

SECTION FOCUS TRANSPARENCY MASTER   **92**

Carbohydrates

**Use with Chapter 24,
Section 24.2**

Sucrose

Starch

Cellulose

❶   Which of these substances can humans use as food?

❷   Why can't humans use corncobs for food?

SECTION FOCUS TRANSPARENCY MASTER (93)

Lipids

Use with Chapter 24, Section 24.3

Vegetable oil

Vegetable shortening

❶ What do the two substances have in common? How do they differ?

❷ How does hydrogenation affect the melting point of vegetable oil?

SECTION FOCUS TRANSPARENCY MASTER

94

DNA

**Use with Chapter 24,
Section 24.4**

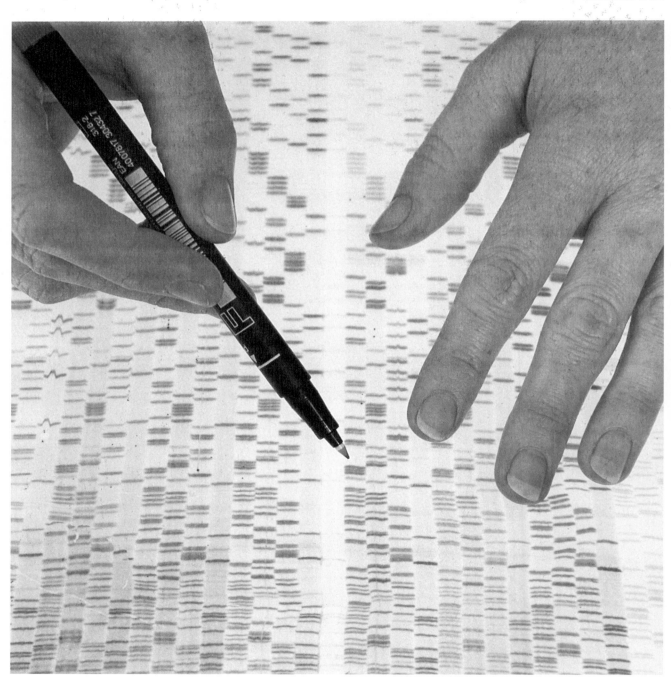

❶ How do you think DNA is like a fingerprint?

❷ How do you think DNA is used in police work?

SECTION FOCUS TRANSPARENCY MASTER

Metabolism

❶ How do you think plants obtain the energy and chemical building blocks they need for growth?

❷ How do you think animals obtain the energy and chemical building blocks they need for growth?

Chemistry: Matter and Change • Chapter 24

SECTION FOCUS TRANSPARENCY MASTER 96

Medical Uses of Nuclear Radiation

Use with Chapter 25, Section 25.1

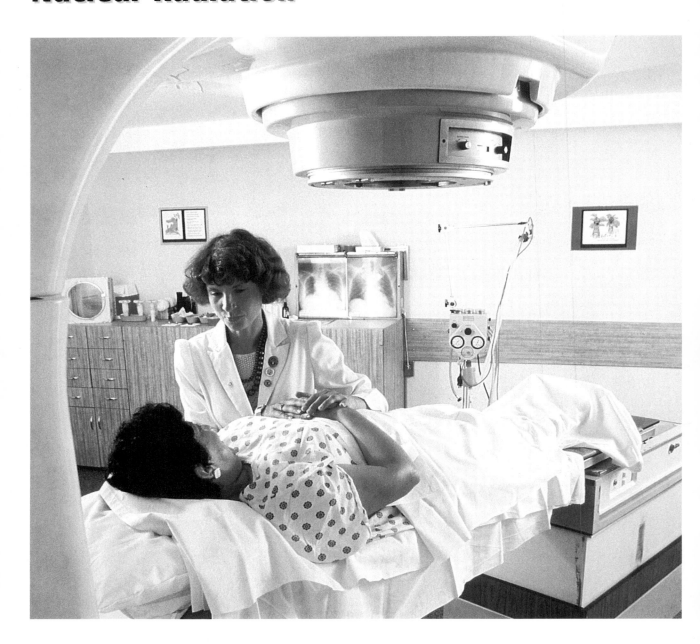

❶ How is nuclear radiation being used for the treatment of this patient?

❷ What risks are involved in using nuclear radiation for the treatment of diseases?

SECTION FOCUS TRANSPARENCY MASTER **97**

Instability

Use with Chapter 25,
Section 25.2

❶ Why is the rock formation in this photograph considered
to be unstable?

❷ How and when will the rock formation become stable?

SECTION FOCUS TRANSPARENCY MASTER 98

Chemical Change or Nuclear Change?

Use with Chapter 25, Section 25.3

❶ Does the photo illustrate a chemical change or a nuclear change?

❷ How is a nuclear change similar to a chemical change? How is it different?

Nuclear Reactions and Energy

**Use with Chapter 25,
Section 25.4**

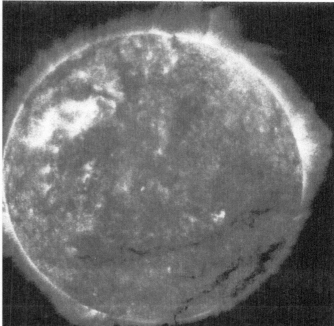

❶ What are some similarities between a nuclear explosion
and the Sun?

❷ What are some differences?

Name _____ Date _____ Class _____

Using Radioisotopes

❶ What type of radiation can penetrate the soil and the steel drums?

❷ What is this man doing?

Effects of Changes in Earth's Atmosphere

Use with Chapter 26, Section 26.1

❶ These trees were damaged by pollution. How is that possible in a large natural area such as a forest?

❷ What kind of pollution do you think damaged these trees?

SECTION FOCUS TRANSPARENCY MASTER **102**

Uses of Freshwater

Use with Chapter 26,
Section 26.2

❶ How is water being used in these photographs?

❷ For each purpose shown, how much water do you think
you use in one day?

SECTION FOCUS TRANSPARENCY MASTER (103)

Mineral Resources

Use with Chapter 26,
Section 26.3

❶ What activity is shown in this photograph?

❷ In what ways can this activity damage the environment?

SECTION FOCUS TRANSPARENCY MASTER 104

Earth as a Greenhouse

**Use with Chapter 26,
Section 26.4**

❶ Why do plants grow well in a greenhouse when the weather is cold outside?

❷ What properties of glass make it suitable for use in a greenhouse?

SECTION FOCUS TRANSPARENCIES
Teacher Guide

1 Protection from the Sun
Use with Chapter 1, Section 1.1

Purpose

▸ To express the need to be protected from the Sun's ultraviolet radiation

Teaching Suggestions

▸ Project the transparency, and have students answer the questions.

▸ Encourage students to list other ways of protecting their skin from exposure to ultraviolet radiation. Students may suggest wearing a hat, long sleeves, sunglasses, and other protective clothing; staying indoors or in the shade between 10:00 A.M. and 2:00 P.M.; and avoiding sunbathing, sunlamps, and tanning salons.

▸ Point out that the atmosphere provides an additional protection against ultraviolet radiation—the ozone layer. Ask students what they know about the ozone layer. Explain that the thinning of the ozone layer in the atmosphere may be one cause of the rising incidence of skin cancer.

▸ Tell students that in this section they will learn more about atmospheric ozone, its depletion, and the protection it provides Earth.

▸ *Answers to questions on the transparency include:*
   1. The people are putting on sunscreen.
   2. Ultraviolet radiation from the Sun can cause the skin to burn or blister and may lead to skin cancer.

2 Weight and Mass
Use with Chapter 1, Section 1.2

Purpose

▸ To contrast weight and mass

Teaching Suggestions

▸ Project the transparency. Ask students to speculate how walking on the Moon might feel different from walking on Earth and to give possible reasons.

▸ Have students answer the questions on the transparency. Ask them to give reasons for their answers. Explain to students that there is a difference between weight and mass. A person's weight is a result of gravitational pull on his or her body. Gravitational pull varies. For example, the gravitational pull on the surface of the Moon is about 1/6 that of Earth at its surface. Thus, a person standing on the moon weighs 1/6 of what he or she weighs on Earth. Mass is a measure of the amount of matter that makes up an object. Mass does not depend on gravitational pull. Thus, a person's mass is the same regardless of where he or she is located.

▸ *Answers to questions on the transparency include:*
   1. The astronaut weighs less on the Moon than on Earth.
   2. The astronaut's mass is the same on the Moon and on Earth.

3 What's killing the plants?
Use with Chapter 1, Section 1.3

Purpose

▸ To pose a problem that can be solved using a scientific method

Teaching Suggestions

▸ Project the transparency, and encourage students who have experience working with plants or have a knowledge of plants to share any information they know about plant diseases and pests.

▸ After students have answered the questions, point out that many problems can be solved by performing tests or experiments. Tell students that scientists use a systemic approach, called a scientific method, to solve problems. The common steps of a scientific method are discussed in Section 1.3.

▸ After students have read this section, you might want them to outline a scientific method they could use to determine what had harmed the plant shown on the transparency.

▸ *Answer to questions on the transparency include:*
   1. It has been attacked by pests.
   2. Answers will vary. Students might suggest growing samples of the same type of plant under different environmental conditions, such as varying amounts of water or light; exposing samples of the plant to organisms, such as certain fungi, that cause plant diseases; or growing samples in the presence of various insect pests.

4 Scientific Research

Use with Chapter 1, Section 1.4

Purpose

▶ To introduce the distinction between pure research and applied research

Teaching Suggestions

▶ Project the transparency, and ask students to describe what is shown.

▶ Have students answer the questions on the transparency as part of a class discussion. Point out that scientists carry out research for different reasons. Some scientists simply enjoy the process of discovery and figuring things out. This type of research is referred to as pure research. Other scientists conduct applied research, in which they try to solve specific problems in order to benefit people or the environment.

▶ After students read about the difference between pure research and applied research in this section, ask them to give examples of each type of research.

▶ *Answers to questions on the transparency include:*
  1. Accept all reasonable answers, such as the scientist is testing the water for pollutants, temperature, oxygen levels, or the presence of water organisms.
  2. Accept all reasonable answers. For example, students may suggest that the scientist's research can help maintain a safe water supply for surrounding communities, protect water organisms from pollutants, or provide a desirable environment for recreational purposes.

5 SI Units

Use with Chapter 2, Section 2.1

Purpose

▶ To show students that they already use SI units

Teaching Suggestions

▶ Project the transparency, and have students categorize the information presented in the scoreboard.

▶ Encourage students to think about how different things are measured. Ask students what units are used in the scoreboard. Could the jumps be measured in different units? If so, which units? (Students might suggest centimeters, feet, yards, inches, etc.)

▶ Most students will have heard of SI units. Have students make a list of SI units and the things they can be used to measure. If students have a difficult time getting started, you might let them begin by listing any units and then classifying them as either SI or English.

▶ Many people feel uncomfortable using SI units because they are more familiar with English units. Encourage a student who has lived in a country that uses SI units to share his or her experience learning English units.

▶ Ask students to point out other things commonly measured using SI units. For example, sports events such as the javelin and the shot put, are measured in meters while running and cycling races are measured in kilometers. Soft drinks are sold in liter containers. Tell students that in this section they will learn more about SI units.

▶ *Answers to questions on the transparency include:*
  1. The person with the longest jump was the winner. In this case, the winner was J. Faklaris with a jump of 7.15 meters.
  2. Answers will vary. Some common comparisons may be to the length of a car, the width of a room, or the length of a chalkboard.

6 How much is it?

Use with Chapter 2, Section 2.2

Purpose

To introduce the concept of conversion factors

Teaching Suggestions

▶ Project the transparency, and have students describe the currency shown.

▶ Tell students to think about how many pennies, dimes, nickels, and quarters are in one dollar. You may want to have students write these amounts down as ratios, so you can later point out that their ratios are conversion factors similar to the SI conversion factors in the chapter.

▶ Have students answer the questions.

▶ Encourage students to point out other conversions that they do on a regular basis. For example, students probably automatically convert minutes to hours, inches to feet, teaspoons to tablespoons, etc. Link these automatic conversions to dimensional analysis. Then tell students that in this section they will learn more about converting SI units.

▶ *Answers to questions on the transparency include:*
1. There are 50 dimes in $5.
2. There are 80 quarters in $20.

7 Who is the better player?
Use with Chapter 2, Section 2.3

Purpose

▶ To introduce the concepts of accuracy and precision

Teaching Suggestions

▶ Project the transparency, and have students describe the game shown.

▶ Encourage students to describe each player's game using the terms *consistent throw* and *good* or *accurate throw*. Lead students to realize that a consistent throw can still be off-target. Ask if a player can be consistently bad? (yes)

▶ Have students list professional athletes that they admire. Then have them describe each athlete's performance in his or her respective sport. Ask what makes professional athletes successful? (They play well, but they also play well consistently.)

▶ Have students answer the questions, then tell them that in this section they will learn that consistent and accurate data in chemistry are important.

▶ You may want to return to this transparency after students have encountered the concepts of accuracy and precision in this section. Have students describe the scenario using these terms.

▶ *Answers to questions on the transparency include:*
1. Students should recognize that the player whose rings are around the stake is the winner of this round.
2. Students should recognize that the player whose rings are around and close to the stake has a better—more accurate—throw.

8 Representing Data
Use with Chapter 2, Section 2.4

Purpose

▶ To introduce the idea that data can be organized into graphs

Teaching Suggestions

▶ Project the transparency, and have students describe the image shown. Make sure that students understand that it is a rain gauge and that the liquid contained within is rainwater.

▶ Have students answer the questions, then tell students that in this section they will learn different ways of representing data.

▶ If time permits, you might allow students to generate different graphs of the data given and determine the effectiveness of each one. Return to this transparency after students have learned about circle graphs, bar graphs, and line graphs. Ask students to suggest which type of graph would provide a better representation of the data.

▶ *Answers to questions on the transparency include:*
1. Sunday received the most rain.
2. Answers will vary. Students might suggest graphing the data or arranging it by the amount of rainfall rather than by days of the week.

9 States of Matter
Use with Chapter 3, Section 3.1

Purpose

▶ To introduce the different states of matter and the concepts of physical property and chemical property

Teaching Suggestions

▶ Project the transparency, and have students describe the contents shown in each photograph.

▶ Encourage students to think about how ice cubes form in an ice tray and what happens when an ice cube melts. Ask students whether melted ice is water. (yes)

▶ Have students answer the questions. Explain that practically all matter exists as either a liquid, a solid, or a gas. You might want to challenge students to describe or name different physical states of another substance, such as carbon dioxide. (gas, dry ice)

▶ Use students' responses to the questions to begin a discussion of physical properties and chemical properties of matter.

▶ *Answers to questions on the transparency include:*
1. The matter shown in each photograph is a form of water.

2. The water is in a different form in each photograph. It is liquid in the photograph on the left, solid in the photograph on the right, and gaseous in the bottom photograph.

10 Physical and Chemical Changes
Use with Chapter 3, Section 3.2

Purpose
▶ To contrast different kinds of changes that matter can undergo

Teaching Suggestions
▶ Project the transparency, and have students describe the two actions shown.

▶ Encourage students to focus on the composition of the tree before and after each action. Ask students whether the chemical substances that make up the tree change as it is cut. (no) What is left after the tree is cut? (pieces of the same tree) Do chemical substances of the tree change as it burns? (yes) What is left after the tree burns? (ashes)

▶ After students answer the questions, point out that the word *burn* is a hint that a change in the substances that make up the tree is taking place. Tell students that in this section they will learn about several different kinds of changes that matter can undergo and certain descriptive words that can help them identify each kind of change.

▶ *Answers to questions on the transparency include:*
  1. When the tree is cut, it becomes two or more pieces. However, it can still be recognized as a tree. The burning tree becomes ashes. The tree no longer looks or functions as a tree after it is burned.
  2. The cutting of the tree shows a change in the shape and size of the tree. The burning of the tree shows a change in the substances that make up the tree.

11 Mixtures
Use with Chapter 3, Section 3.3

Purpose
▶ To distinguish between a pure substance and a mixture and to provide examples of different kinds of mixtures

Teaching Suggestions
▶ Project the transparency, and have students tell whether each item shown consists of one substance or more than one substance.

▶ Ask students to explain what they think a mixture is. Lead students to understand that a mixture is a blend of two or more substances. Point out that some mixtures have a uniform composition, whereas others do not.

▶ After students answer the questions, encourage them to give other examples of mixtures. Then have them read in this section about different kinds of mixtures.

▶ *Answers to questions on the transparency include:*
  1. The substances in the tea bag are dissolved in hot water.
  2. Photograph A: The substance is uniform in color and consistency. It is transparent. Photograph C: The substance is a mixture of separate components.

12 Common Elements and Compounds
Use with Chapter 3, Section 3.4

Purpose
▶ To link the elements in the periodic table to familiar substances and compounds

Teaching Suggestions
▶ Project the transparency, and have students describe the information in the pie chart.

▶ Focus students' attention on the title of the graph. Then ask the following questions: What does the entire circle represent? (the elements found in Earth's crust) Does this graph show every element in Earth's crust? (No, some elements occur in amounts smaller than those shown.)

▶ Have students answer the questions posed on the transparency. You may want to make a master list of common items and their constituent elements for question 2. As a class, add to the list to emphasize the most common elements.

▶ Lead students to conclude that a small number of elements combine to make up many of the substances that are familiar to them. Point out that hydrogen is the most common element in the universe and that 74.3% of Earth's crust is just two elements (oxygen and silicon). You might also point out that living things are made up mostly of four elements (carbon, hydrogen, oxygen, and nitrogen).

▶ *Answers to questions on the transparency include:*

1. Oxygen is the most abundant element in Earth's crust.

2. Answers include the following: oxygen—water; calcium—chalk; sodium—salt; magnesium—Epsom's salt; silicon—silicon dioxide (sand).

13 Gold Atoms

Use with Chapter 4, Section 4.1

Purpose

▶ To introduce the concept of atoms

Teaching Suggestions

▶ Project the transparency, and encourage students to think about what happens when a substance is broken down into smaller and smaller pieces. For example, does the gold in gold nuggets behave the same way chemically as the gold in a gold bar?

▶ After students have answered the questions, point out that atoms are the smallest particles of an element that retain the properties of the element.

▶ Tell students that in this section they will learn about the history of the atom and about different atomic theories of the past.

▶ *Answers to questions on the transparency include:*

1. Yes; all three forms of gold are yellow in color, solid at room temperature, and undergo the same chemical changes.

2. Answers may vary. Some students may say yes because they have already studied subatomic particles; others may say no because they know that even a gold atom retains the properties of gold.

14 Models of an Atom

Use with Chapter 4, Section 4.2

Purpose

▶ To introduce the structure of the atom and positions of the subatomic particles

Teaching Suggestions

▶ Project the transparency, and tell students that the photographs represent different models of an atom.

▶ Have students answer the questions. Then ask them to think about what the two models might indicate about the structure of atoms. For example, are atoms solid spheres? What might the chocolate chips represent? Do atoms have a dense nucleus?

▶ Tell students that in this section they will learn about subatomic particles—particles that make up atoms.

▶ *Answers to questions on the transparency include:*

1. Both are solid spheres.

2. The peach model is a rigid solid, whereas the chocolate-chip dough model is a flexible solid. The peach model has a central nucleus, the peach pit. The dough model has particles, the chips, scattered throughout.

15 Atoms and Elements

Use with Chapter 4, Section 4.3

Purpose

▶ To illustrate that atomic differences between elements result in differences in the elements' physical and chemical properties

Teaching Suggestions

▶ Project the transparency, and have students describe the two elements, sodium and sulfur. Tell students that the information next to each element is from the periodic table. Point out the placement of the two elements in the periodic table. Students should note that sodium and sulfur are in the same period but in different groups.

▶ Have students answer the questions, which are open-ended. You might want to go around the room and have students share their answers, listing the answers on the chalkboard or on a transparency.

▶ Tell students that they will learn in this section what the numbers next to the two elements on the transparency mean. After students have read this section, you might want to return to the transparency and have students compare the atomic numbers and atomic masses of sodium and sulfur. Lead them to conclude that the two elements differ by the number of protons and electrons. This difference between the elements results in their different chemical and physical properties.

▶ *Answers to questions on the transparency include:*

1. Accept all reasonable differences. Possibilities include the following: Sodium is softer than sulfur. Sodium is an alkali metal, and sulfur is a nonmetal. Sodium's atomic number is 11, and sulfur's is 16.

Sodium's atomic weight is 22.990, and sulfur's is 32.066.

2. Accept all reasonable responses. The atoms differ in their numbers of protons, electrons, and neutrons; name, and placement on the periodic table.

16 Radiation
Use with Chapter 4, Section 4.4

Purpose

▶ To introduce the concept of radioactivity

Teaching Suggestions

▶ Project the transparency, and encourage students to think about where they may have seen this symbol. Students may have seen it in a medical or dental setting, such as where X rays or PET scans are used. They may have seen this symbol at a university or laboratory setting, where radiation is used to do research. They also may have seen the symbol in news reports about nuclear power plants, historical accounts, or nuclear accidents. You may want to encourage students to make a list and discuss what these places have in common.

▶ Have students answer the questions, then point out that this symbol is a warning. Have students brainstorm and then research what safety precautions this warning should elicit.

▶ Ask students why there is a need for this symbol. Lead them to understand that radiation is invisible, odorless, and hard to detect with the senses alone.

▶ Tell students that in this section they will learn how radiation was discovered and the different kinds of radiation.

▶ *Answers to questions on the transparency include:*

1. Answers will vary. Some students may recognize the symbol as the international symbol for radioactive materials.

2. Answers will vary. Students should realize that the symbol is a warning and that they must take precautions to protect themselves from radiation exposure.

17 Light Waves
Use with Chapter 5, Section 5.1

Purpose

▶ To introduce the concept of electromagnetic waves

Teaching Suggestions

▶ Project the transparency, and encourage students to describe different rainbows they have seen. Ask: When did the rainbow appear? How was it similar to the rainbow in the photograph? How was it different?

▶ Have students answer the questions. Make a list of students' responses to the second question and have students categorize the different types of waves on the list. (Students might suggest categorizing the waves into those that are visible and those that are invisible. They might also categorize the waves into electromagnetic and nonelectromagnetic waves. Allow students to make suggestions freely as they consider the differences in the types of waves.) After students have read the section, you might return to the list again and have students categorize the waves to see whether their answers change.

▶ Point out that light is visible electromagnetic waves. Other electromagnetic waves, such as microwaves and radio waves, are not visible.

▶ Tell students that in this section they will learn about the characteristics of electromagnetic waves.

▶ *Answers to questions on the transparency include:*

1. Students may say light from the Sun (or light waves) and rain.

2. Answers may include radio waves, microwaves, sound waves, ocean waves, and so on.

18 Atomic Orbitals
Use with Chapter 5, Section 5.2

Purpose

▶ To introduce the concept of atomic orbitals

Teaching Suggestions

▶ Project the transparency, and have students answer the questions. Ask them why it takes more energy for the painter to climb to the top rung of the ladder. (The painter is moving farther away from Earth's surface climbing to the top rung.) Then ask why the paintbrush hits the ground with more energy when it falls from the top rung. (The paintbrush had more potential energy at the top of the ladder.)

▶ Tell students that the electrons of an atom occupy orbitals around the atom's nucleus that are similar to the rungs of a ladder. For example, just as a person cannot step between the rungs of a ladder, an electron cannot occupy the space between the atom's orbitals. Also, it takes energy for an electron to move from an orbital close to the atom's nucleus to an orbital farther from the nucleus, just as it takes energy to move up the rungs of a ladder.

▶ Tell students that orbitals that are farther from an atom's nucleus are higher-energy orbitals. Ask students to predict what happens when an electron drops from a higher-energy orbital to a lower-energy orbital. Have them base their prediction on their answer to the second question on the transparency. Lead students to recognize that the electron will release energy. The greater the distance between orbitals, the more energy is released.

▶ Have students recall what they read about atomic emission spectra in the previous section. Tell them that in this section they will learn how the movements of electrons from higher-energy orbitals to lower-energy orbitals create a unique atomic emission spectrum for each element.

▶ *Answers to questions on the transparency include:*
  1. It takes more energy to climb to the top rung of the ladder.
  2. The paintbrush hit the ground with more energy when it fell from the top rung of the ladder.

19 Electron Configurations

Use with Chapter 5, Section 5.3

Purpose

▶ To introduce the aufbau principle

Teaching Suggestions

▶ Project the transparency, and have students describe the photograph.

▶ Ask students if they have bought tickets for a concert or sports event lately and whether there was a range in the prices of the tickets. Point out that ticket pricing takes into account how far from the stage, field, or court a seat is, whether a seat is in the middle of a row or at the end of a row, and whether there are objects obstructing the view from a seat.

▶ Have students answer the questions. Then ask: Which electrons have more energy? (The electrons in energy levels farthest from the nucleus have more energy than those closest to the nucleus.) Point out that just as it takes more energy to climb to the arena seats that are in upper rows, it takes more energy for an electron to "climb" to an orbital that is in an energy level far from the nucleus.

▶ Tell students that in this section they will learn about different rules that govern which energy level and which orbital an electron will occupy in an atom. One of those rules is called the aufbau principle, which states that an electron will occupy the lowest energy orbital available. Ask students to assume that they are the first person to enter the arena shown on the photograph and to tell which seat they would sit in if they had to follow the aufbau principle. (the seat closest to center court)

▶ *Answers to questions on the transparency include:*
  1. Those seats closest to the center of the court are in greater demand.
  2. The rows of seats represent energy levels. The actual seats represent individual orbitals.

20 Classification

Use with Chapter 6, Section 6.1

Purpose

▶ To illustrate the usefulness of classification

Teaching Suggestions

▶ Project the transparency, and have students identify various materials they can find in a library (for example, books, magazines, newspapers, videos) and describe how they are grouped.

▶ After students have answered the questions, ask if they are familiar with the classification system that their school or local library uses to shelve books. If so, have a volunteer explain the system. (Fiction books are shelved alphabetically by author. Nonfiction books are shelved either by the Dewey Decimal Classification or the Library of Congress Subject Headings. Both systems are hierarchical. For example, in the Dewey Decimal Classification, materials related to chemistry have call numbers between 540 and 549. The first digit, 5, indicates that the subject is mathematics or natural sciences; the second digit, 4, indicates chemistry and its related fields; and the third digit, 0–9, indicates specific topics such as inorganic, organic, or physical chemistry. Letters and numbers after the decimal point indicate further levels of classification. In the Library of Congress Subject Headings, materials related to chemistry have the initial call letters QD. (Q indicates that the subject is mathematics or natural sciences, with D pertaining to chemistry and its related fields. Numbers and letters that follow QD indicate further levels of classification.)

▶ Tell students that in this section they will learn how scientists classify elements.

▶ *Answers to questions on the transparency include:*

   1. Most nonfiction books are classified by subject. Fiction books are classified by author.

   2. The classification system makes locating a specific book or browsing for a book on a particular subject easier to do.

21 Cycles

Use with Chapter 6, Section 6.2

Purpose

▶ To review the concept of periodicity of elements

Teaching Suggestions

▶ Project the transparency, and point out the sequence of three photographs showing a northeastern forest at different times of the year. Ask students to identify the season that each photograph represents and for the clues that they used to identify the season.

▶ After students have answered the questions, encourage them to name some other natural cycles. (lunar cycle, tidal cycle, and Earth year) Ask students how the elements in the periodic table also follow a cycle. (Students should recall from the previous section that there is a periodic repetition of the elements' chemical and physical properties.) Tell students that in this section they will learn why the elements show a periodic repetition of characteristics.

▶ *Answers to questions on the transparency include:*

   1. The photographs represent the cycle of the seasons.

   2. The missing photograph should show the forest in spring. The seasons are a periodic event, with the pattern of summer, fall, winter, and spring repeated annually.

22 Inferring Characteristics

Use with Chapter 6, Section 6.3

Purpose

▶ To introduce the concept that the physical and chemical characteristics of an element can be inferred from its position in the periodic table

Teaching Suggestions

▶ Project the transparency, and tell students that the photo illustrates the arrangement of football players in an offensive line. (The arrangement is called an I formation.) You may wish to have students discuss some of the fundamentals of football.

▶ After students have answered the questions, ask them to identify other team sports in which the characteristics of a player can be inferred from the position played. (basketball, relay swimming, and soccer)

▶ Tell students that in this section they will learn about some kinds of characteristics of elements that can be inferred from the elements' positions in the periodic table.

▶ *Answers to questions on the transparency include:*

   1. The quarterback determines the strategies to move the ball forward and throws or hands off the ball to another player. Since the center, guards, and tackles are in front of the quarterback, they keep members of the opposing team away from the quarterback by blocking them. The fullback and halfback are behind the quarterback, so they are free to carry the ball and block. The wide receivers and tight end move ahead of the quarterback to receive passes.

   2. Quarterbacks must be agile, quick, and have a good throwing arm. Centers, guards, and tackles must be massive and strong. Fullbacks and halfbacks must be strong and have some speed and some agility. Wide receivers and tight ends must have speed and agility.

23 s-Block Elements

Use with Chapter 7, Section 7.1

Purpose

▶ To introduce the concept that the properties of the s-block elements vary in a regular way

Teaching Suggestions

▶ Project the transparency, and ask students to identify what is shown on the transparency (strips from a paint-color chart showing different shades of blue) and to describe how they are used (to select a desired shade of blue paint).

▶ Ask students to think about how the organization of colors in a paint-color chart might be similar to the organization of elements in the periodic table. Then have students answer the questions.

▶ Emphasize that the periodic table is not just a listing of the elements. Rather, the specific order of the elements in the periodic table makes it a tool that can be used to find an element with certain desired properties. Just as one can use a paint-color chart to find a certain shade of paint, the periodic table can be used to find an element with a high or low boiling point, atomic radius, etc.

▶ *Answers to questions on the transparency include:*
   1. Both color strips show different shades of the color blue, with the shades decreasing in darkness going down each strip. The shades in the two strips are of slightly different hues of blue.
   2. The elements in the two columns are related but show somewhat different properties. The properties of the elements within each column are more similar, varying slightly in a regular way going down the column.

24 Noble Gases

Use with Chapter 7, Section 7.2

Purpose

▶ To introduce one group of the p-block elements, the noble gases

Teaching Suggestions

▶ Project the transparency, and ask students to identify the type of light shown. (neon light) Have students recall from Chapter 5 that a neon sign produces light when excited neon atoms in the tube release energy.

▶ After students have answered the questions, tell them that so-called neon lights that emit colors other than red include other elements from group 8A. For example, argon emits blue light, and helium emits yellow light. Remind students at this time that all group 8A elements are gases, called noble gases.

▶ Tell students that in this section they will learn about the group 8A elements and other elements that belong

to the p-block of the periodic table. Have students locate the p-block elements on the periodic table. Emphasize that these elements show a wide range of properties from group to group.

▶ *Answers to questions on the transparency include:*
   1. The element is neon, located in group 8A of the periodic table.
   2. The other elements in group 8A are most similar to neon.

25 Transition Elements

Use with Chapter 7, Section 7.3

Purpose

▶ To introduce transition elements, which make up the d-block and f-block of the periodic table

Teaching Suggestions

▶ Project the transparency, and direct students' attention to the compositions of the coins. Ask students to describe the properties of gold and silver. Then have them answer the questions.

▶ Ask students which elements in the periodic table have properties similar to those of gold and silver. (Transition elements in group 1B have properties similar to gold and silver.)

▶ Have students write the electron configurations for gold and silver and explain how the elements' electron configurations differ from those of the elements they have studied so far. (The final electron of gold and silver enters a d sublevel.) Tell students that in this section they will learn about elements in the d-block and f-block of the periodic table, which are called transition elements and include gold and silver.

▶ *Answers to questions on the transparency include:*
   1. Answers will vary. Students may say that gold and silver are strong metals that last a long time and that they can be easily shaped into coins.
   2. Answers will vary. Gold is used in jewelry, electrical and electronic devices, and dental crowns. Silver is used in jewelry, electrical and electronic devices, housewares, and dental fillings.

26 Formation of Ions
Use with Chapter 8, Section 8.1

Purpose

▶ To introduce the formation of ions by the addition or removal of electrons

Teaching Suggestions

▶ Ask students to recall how much charge each of these atomic particles carries: proton ($+1$), electron (-1), neutron (0). Then project the transparency and have students answer the questions. Follow up the second question by asking what would happen to the overall charge on an atom if the atom gained or lost one or more electrons. (The charge would be -1 or $+1$ times the number of electrons that were gained or lost, respectively.)

▶ Remind students that some atoms achieve a more stable electron structure by gaining one or more valence electrons, while other atoms achieve stability by losing one or more electrons. Emphasize that the number of protons in the nucleus does not change when electrons are gained or lost. Add that an atom with an unequal number of protons and electrons is called an ion.

▶ *Answers to questions on the transparency include:*
1. The masses on each pan are equal, so the system is balanced. The numbers of electrons and protons in an atom are equal, so the atom is uncharged.
2. The system would become unbalanced. The pan with the greater mass would be lower.

27 Forming Rust
Use with Chapter 8, Section 8.2

Purpose

▶ To introduce the concept of ionic bonding between metals and nonmetals

Teaching Suggestions

▶ Project the transparency, and point out that the nail on the top would become like the nail on the bottom if exposed to moist air for a long time.

▶ After students have answered the questions, point out that the chemical reaction that had occurred involved a specific type of bonding, which students will read about in this section of the chapter. Like all bonding, it involved electrical attractions between particles.

▶ *Answers to questions on the transparency include:*
1. The nail on the top is shiny, hard, and strong. The nail on the bottom is rusty and brittle.
2. Answers will vary. The element iron in the nail reacted with the element oxygen in moist air to form rust, which is a reddish compound.

28 Combining Objects
Use with Chapter 8, Section 8.3

Purpose

▶ To introduce the writing of formulas for combinations of objects, an approach that can be applied to atoms in compounds

Teaching Suggestions

▶ Before projecting the transparency, explain that letter abbreviations and numbers can be used to express combinations of objects in shorthand form. Then project the transparency, and direct students' attention to the letter abbreviations for the articles of clothing and for the clothespins.

▶ After students have answered the questions, explain that letter abbreviations and numbers can also be used to write formulas for chemical compounds, which are made up of various numbers of atoms.

▶ *Answers to questions on the transparency include:*
1. A: one pair of pants and two clothespins; B: one pair of pants and one clothespin; C: one sock and one clothespin; D: two socks and one clothespin.
2. X = pants, Y = clothespins, Z = sock; XY_2, XY, XZ, XZ_2.

29 Properties of Metals
Use with Chapter 8, Section 8.4

Purpose

▶ To introduce properties that are characteristic of metallic elements, including malleability and ductility

Teaching Suggestions

▶ Project the transparency, and ask students to describe what they see and to think about the uses and properties of metals.

▶ After students have answered the questions, ask them to name other metals and to consider the importance of metals in modern society.

▶ *Answers to questions on the transparency include:*

1. Copper is shown. It is shiny (metallic luster).

2. The metals are being hammered, which shows that metals are malleable.

30 A Special Kind of "Ice"
Use with Chapter 9, Section 9.1

Purpose

▶ To introduce the concept of covalent bonding

Teaching Suggestions

▶ Project the transparency, and ask students where they may have seen this substance before. They should notice that the dry ice is not melting. You may wish to explain that it is changing directly to gas.

▶ Direct students' attention to the carbon dioxide model shown, then have them answer the questions. Tell students that the model represents the structure of the carbon dioxide molecules that make up dry ice. Point out the bonds between the atoms of the carbon dioxide molecule. Explain that the bonds are called covalent bonds and are different from ionic bonds, which students learned about in the previous chapter. Tell students that in this section they will read about covalent bonds.

▶ *Answers to questions on the transparency include:*

1. It is called dry ice and is commonly used to keep materials such as ice cream very cold.

2. Dry ice is carbon dioxide, consisting of bonded carbon and oxygen atoms, rather than the hydrogen and oxygen atoms present in ordinary ice, which is a form of water.

31 What's in a name?
Use with Chapter 9, Section 9.2

Purpose

▶ To introduce prefixes used in naming compounds

Teaching Suggestions

▶ Project the transparency, and ask students to name the various objects shown. Also ask them to look for things in common among the names.

▶ After students have answered the questions, point out that prefixes, or beginning syllables, such as *mono-*

and *tri-* are also used in naming chemical compounds because they reveal how many atoms of each type are present.

▶ *Answers to questions on the transparency include:*

1. The objects include a big wheel (type of tricycle), octopus, pentagon, and monocle.

2. The first few letters reveal information about number. For example, *tri-* in *tricycle* refers to the presence of three wheels. *Mono-* refers to one, *penta-* refers to five, and *octo-* refers to eight.

32 Combining Units
Use with Chapter 9, Section 9.3

Purpose

▶ To introduce the idea of combining small units, such as atoms, to build larger ones, such as molecules

Teaching Suggestions

▶ Project the transparency, and direct students' attention to the process being shown and to the characteristics of the construction units that are being used, including the way they are designed to lock into one another.

▶ After students have answered the questions, pass around a model of a relatively large molecule, and have students note the similarity between the model and the construction shown in the transparency. (Both are made of smaller units connected together.)

▶ *Answers to questions on the transparency include:*

1. The small construction-set units are being used to build a larger object.

2. They are able to attach or connect to one another.

33 Taking Up Space
Use with Chapter 9, Section 9.4

Purpose

▶ To introduce the idea that objects, including orbitals in the VSEPR model, tend to fill space so that they maximize the distance between them

Teaching Suggestions

▶ Project the transparency, and ask students to describe what they see.

▶ After students have answered the questions, remind them that the electrons in atoms occupy orbitals. Point out that because electrons are oppositely charged, the orbitals tend to push away from each other and assume positions as far as possible from each other.

▶ Tell students that in this section they will learn how the orbitals of molecules lead to molecular shapes that are similar to the balloon shapes shown in the transparency.

▶ *Answers to questions on the transparency include:*

1. Balloons (two, then three, then four) have been tied together at the neck, forming various shapes.

2. The two balloons form a linear arrangement. The three balloons form a planar triangular arrangement. The four balloons form a tetrahedral arrangement. In each case, the balloons take up positions as far away as possible from each other.

34 Tug-of-War
Use with Chapter 9, Section 9.5

Purpose

▶ To introduce the concept of electronegativity as a "pull" for shared electrons

Teaching Suggestions

▶ Project the transparency, and ask students to analyze what is occurring.

▶ After students have answered the questions, lead them to recall that covalently bonded atoms each attract the electrons they share. Ask students to think about what might happen if the attractions are unequal. (The shared electrons spend more time around the atom that has a greater attraction for the electrons.)

▶ *Answers to questions on the transparency include:*

1. A tug-of-war contest is taking place, in which two teams pull in opposite directions on the same rope.

2. Eventually one team will weaken, or lose energy. The other team will then pull much more of the rope toward itself, so the sharing will not be equal.

35 Evidence of Chemical Change
Use with Chapter 10, Section 10.1

Purpose

▶ To introduce evidence of chemical change and its effect on the identity of a substance

Teaching Suggestions

▶ Project the transparency, then show students actual items that have undergone chemical changes along with identical items that have not. Examples include shiny and rusty nails, rotten and ripe fruit, burned and unburned matches, and raw and cooked food. Caution students not to touch or taste any items that could be potentially hazardous, such as food items.

▶ Have students compare and contrast the items brought to class. From students' comments, develop a list that describes the changes these items have undergone. Students will probably notice changes in odor, color, texture, and consistency.

▶ *Answers to questions on the transparency include:*

1. Students should notice irreversible changes of color and odor.

2. Because of differences in texture, consistency, color, and odor, students should conclude that the identity of the materials involved has changed.

36 Types of Chemical Reactions
Use with Chapter 10, Section 10.2

Purpose

▶ To introduce the concept of classifying chemical reactions by type

Teaching Suggestions

▶ Project the transparency, and discuss with students the questions and their answers. Then, show them the decomposition of hydrogen peroxide into oxygen and water. (Note that placing hydrogen peroxide in contact with something that contains enzymes, such as raw liver, potatoes, or carrots, catalyzes its decomposition.) Have students compare and contrast the corrosion of metal and the decomposition of hydrogen peroxide. Elicit from students that one type of chemical reaction involves the combination of reactants (corrosion) and the other type involves the breaking down of a compound (decomposition).

▶ Show students other examples of simple chemical reactions, such as the combustion of a match or the appearance of copper on an iron nail when placed in a solution of a copper compound. Have them describe similarities and differences among the reactions.

▶ *Answers to questions on the transparency include:*
1. The metals are shiny and smooth with consistent color.
2. The metals combined with gases in the atmosphere, such as oxygen.

37 Solid from Liquids
Use with Chapter 10, Section 10.3

Purpose
▶ To introduce types of reactions that occur in aqueous solution

Teaching Suggestions
▶ Project the transparency, and point out that before mixing, both liquids are clear and colorless, like water. However, the formation of a precipitate shows that the liquids are solutions of compounds, and a chemical change occurs when they are mixed.

▶ If possible, perform a similar formation of a precipitate as a demonstration. A safe example is the mixing of solutions of calcium chloride and sodium carbonate, which forms a white calcium carbonate precipitate.

▶ Adding soap (not detergent) to a solution of magnesium hydroxide or calcium hydroxide also forms a precipitate. Tell students that magnesium hydroxide and calcium hydroxide are compounds found in hard water, and the solid formed is what is commonly known as soap scum.

▶ *Answers to questions on the transparency include:*
1. double replacement
2. The ions in the compounds dissociate in water. They are then able to come in contact with each other, and a precipitate forms if the proper combination of ions forms an insoluble solid.

38 Comparing Counting Units
Use with Chapter 11, Section 11.1

Purpose
▶ To introduce the enormous size of Avogadro's number

Teaching Suggestions
▶ Project the transparency, and have students note the trends in the items' mass, volume, and the numerical value of the counting unit.

▶ After students have answered the questions, tell them that they will learn about the standard numerical value of the counting unit for atoms and molecules in this section.

▶ After Avogadro's number has been introduced, return to the numerical values of the counting units listed on the transparency and have students compare them with the value of Avogadro's number.

▶ *Answers to questions on the transparency include:*
1. As the mass and volume of an item decrease, the size of the numerical value of the counting unit increases.
2. The size of the numerical value of the counting unit would be enormous.

39 Count Per Weight
Use with Chapter 11, Section 11.2

Purpose
▶ To introduce the concept that a mass (weight) measurement of representative particles can be used to indirectly count representative particles

Teaching Suggestions
▶ Project the transparency and explain that shrimp are sold according to count size—the number range of shrimp per pound.

▶ After students have answered the questions, discuss how count size indicates variation in the weights of the shrimp. For example, a 10 count would indicate each shrimp weighs 1.6 ounces, whereas a 10–12 count would indicate that the weights of the shrimp vary between 1.3 and 1.6 ounces.

▶ *Answers to questions on the transparency include:*
1. between 30 and 36 shrimp
2. weight

40 Conservation of Mass
Use with Chapter 11, Section 11.3

Purpose
▶ To introduce students to the concept that stoichiometric calculations are based on the conservation of mass in chemical reactions

Teaching Suggestions

▶ Project the transparency, and explain that a barbell consists of a bar, sleeve, plates, and outside collar held in place by a setscrew. Discuss how a set of plates can be used to make barbells of different masses.

▶ After students have answered the questions, ask them to speculate how the combined mass of one mole of carbon atoms and two moles of oxygen atoms compares with the mass of one mole of carbon dioxide molecules. (The two masses are equal.) Tell students that they will learn in this section how to calculate the molar masses of compounds based on the molar masses of the particles that make up the compounds.

▶ *Answers to questions on the transparency include:*
  1. The masses would be equal.
  2. The masses are equal.

41 Percent Composition
Use with Chapter 11, Section 11.4

Purpose

▶ To introduce the concept of percent composition

Teaching Suggestions

▶ Project the transparency, and point out that the bag contains fertilizer, which is mixed with water and added to the soil. Explain that inert materials listed in the contents are inactive materials.

▶ After the students have answered the questions, ask if they think the number of zinc atoms in the contents of the bag is greater than, equal to, or less than the number of manganese atoms. Have students explain their reasoning. (Students should realize that the weight of the zinc atoms (0.05% × 5.0 lb) is equal to the weight of the manganese atoms (0.05% × 5.0 lb). Because the weights are equal, the masses are equal. Because the molar mass of zinc is greater than that of manganese, the number of zinc atoms in the bag is less than the number of manganese atoms.)

▶ *Answers to questions on the transparency include:*
  1. 60.35%; Add the percentages of all the materials except inert materials; subtract the percentage of inert materials from 100%.
  2. 1.5 lb

42 Soaking Up Water
Use with Chapter 11, Section 11.5

Purpose

▶ To introduce the concept of hydrated crystals

Teaching Suggestions

▶ Project the transparency, and point out that natural sponges are the remains of aquatic invertebrates that belong to the Phylum Porifera, which means *pore-bearer.*

▶ After students have answered the questions, ask them what the difference would be between the mass of the wet sponge in the photo and the mass of the same sponge when dry. (The wet sponge would be heavier due to the mass of water absorbed by the sponge.)

▶ *Answers to questions on the transparency include:*
  1. The water comes from small spaces (pores) within the structure of the sponge.
  2. There are spaces among the atoms or ions that make up the crystal in which water molecules can be located.

43 Balancing Reactions
Use with Chapter 12, Section 12.1

Purpose

▶ To illustrate that a balanced equation shows the quantitative relationships among the substances in a reaction

Teaching Suggestions

▶ Project the transparency, and point out the differences among the nut-and-bolt assemblies.

▶ After students have answered the questions, have them code the assemblies as follows: assembly A: WX, assembly B: YZ_2, assembly C: WZ, and assembly D: YX_2. Help students recognize that the letter W represents the long shank, Y for the short shank. X represents the rectangular nut, Z the hexagonal nut. Using the code, have students write the equation that represents the reaction.

$$WX + YZ_2 \rightarrow WZ + YX_2$$

By inspection, have them balance the equation.

$$2WX + YZ_2 \rightarrow 2WZ + YX_2$$

▶ *Answers to questions on the transparency include:*
  1. No, there are not enough square nuts.

2. minimum reactant assemblies—Assembly A: 2;
Assembly B: 1
number of product assemblies—Assembly C: 2;
Assembly D: 1

44 Using the Right Amounts
Use with Chapter 12, Section 12.2

Purpose

▸ To introduce the use of ratios in stoichiometric calculations

Teaching Suggestions

▸ Project the transparency, and inquire if students have ever baked cookies. Ask them for evidence that baking cookies involves chemical changes. (Gases evolve, leading to aromas; color and texture changes take place.)

▸ Ask students to compare and contrast the cookie recipe with a balanced chemical equation. Among other things, lead students to recognize that the ingredients and product of the recipe are analogous to the reactants and products of a chemical equation, and the amounts used in the recipe are similar to the coefficients in a chemical equation. However, emphasize that unlike the reactants in a chemical equation, many of the ingredients in the recipe, such as the egg, chocolate chips, and brown sugar, are complex mixtures of different substances. Thus, many complex reactions take place during the baking process.

▸ After students have answered the questions, ask them to predict how doubling the number of moles of reactants in a chemical reaction would affect the number of moles of products. (The number of moles of products would be doubled.)

▸ *Answers to questions on the transparency include:*
  1. 42 chocolate chip cookies
  2. double the amount of each ingredient

45 Limiting Reactants
Use with Chapter 12, Section 12.3

Purpose

▸ To introduce the concept of limiting reactants

Teaching Suggestions

▸ Project the transparency, and point out that the fire blanket, along with the shower and fire extinguisher, are important safety devices in the laboratory.

▸ After students have answered the questions, review the proper use of each safety device.

▸ Ask students if they are familiar with the term *smother*. (to kill by depriving of air). Have them discuss how the term might be applied to extinguishing a fire with a fire blanket. (A fire blanket smothers a fire by depriving the combustion reaction of one of the reactants, oxygen.)

▸ *Answers to questions on the transparency include:*
  1. to extinguish burning clothes
  2. Answers may vary. The fire blanket eliminates oxygen from the combustion reaction.

46 Determining Efficiency
Use with Chapter 12, Section 12.4

Purpose

▸ To introduce the concept of percent yield for a chemical reaction

Teaching Suggestions

▸ Project the transparency, and ask students how one determines whether a ballplayer is "good at bat." Lead students to recognize that one way is by comparing the number of times the player had a hit with the number of times she had an opportunity to hit.

▸ Some students may realize that the player's batting efficiency is the player's "batting average," which is expressed as a decimal, such as 0.255. A 0.255 batting average indicates that the player's chance of hitting the ball, based on past performance, is 255 out of 1000.

▸ After students have answered the questions, tell them that in this section they will learn how chemists measure the efficiency of a chemical reaction by calculating percent yield.

▸ *Answers to questions on the transparency include:*
  1. $23/90 \times 100\% = 26\%$
  2. Answers may vary. Chemists compare the actual amount of product produced to the amount of product predicted by stoichiometric calculation.

47 Changes in Air Pressure
Use with Chapter 13, Section 13.1

Purpose
▶ To introduce the concept of changing air pressure

Teaching Suggestions
▶ Project the transparency, and ask students if they have ever experienced having to breathe harder at higher altitudes. Have students speculate why that was the case. Lead them to recognize that breathing harder at high altitudes is due to decreased air pressure, which causes less oxygen to be absorbed by the lungs.

▶ After students have answered the questions, ask them if they know what instrument is used to measure changes in air pressure, which is used to predict changes in weather. (barometer) Tell students that in this section they will learn how a barometer works and about the properties of air and other gases.

▶ *Answers to questions on the transparency include:*
   1. The air pressure will decrease.
   2. With increased altitude, the amount of air pressing down decreases, resulting in decreased air pressure.

48 Forces of Attraction
Use with Chapter 13, Section 13.2

Purpose
▶ To introduce the concept that forces of attraction exist between molecules

Teaching Suggestions
▶ Project the transparency, and ask students to recall electrostatic charges. Have students explain why the items of clothing from the dryer cling to each other. (As the clothes tumbled past each other, some items of clothing gained a static negative charge by gaining stray electrons, whereas other items gained a static positive charge by losing electrons. When the clothes stopped tumbling, the positively and negatively charged items attracted each other.)

▶ After students have answered the questions, point out that the forces of attraction between molecules are electrical in nature. However, unlike the clothes from the dryer, the molecules do not have net static charges; they are electrically neutral.

▶ *Answers to questions on the transparency include:*
   1. Sparks may be seen, and a crackling noise that sometimes accompanies sparks may be heard.
   2. Answers will vary. Students may say that solids do not separate into parts on their own or that liquids flow in a continuous column.

49 Behavior of Liquids
Use with Chapter 13, Section 13.3

Purpose
▶ To extend kinetic-molecular theory to the behavior of liquids

Teaching Suggestions
▶ Project the transparency, and point out that the dishes are soaking in water alone; no detergent has been added to the water. Ask students why swirling the water or repeatedly dunking the dishes that are soaking in water often helps to clean the dishes. (The motion of the water on the dishes helps to break up the food particles on the dish.)

▶ Ask students to think about other ways in which the motion of water molecules can be increased. Have them recall the kinetic-molecular theory discussed in Section 13.1. Then have students answer the questions on the transparency.

▶ *Answers to questions on the transparency include:*
   1. Hot water removes dirt from dishes better than cold water.
   2. Molecules of hot water have greater average kinetic energy and therefore move faster than do molecules of cold water.

50 Changes in States of Matter
Use with Chapter 13, Section 13.4

Purpose
▶ To introduce the concept of phase changes

Teaching Suggestions
▶ Project the transparency, and have students identify the three states of water—ice, liquid water, and water vapor—shown in the photograph.

▶ Ask students to describe the weather conditions suggested by the photograph. For example, does the photograph suggest low or high air temperature, low or high relative humidity, or low or high air pressure? (low air temperature, high relative humidity, low air pressure)

▶ After students have answered the questions, tell them that in this section they will learn how the states of a substance are affected by temperature and pressure.

▶ *Answers to questions on the transparency include:*

  1. The ice indicates that liquid water has changed to solid water. The glistening surface of the ice indicates that solid water has changed to liquid water. The fog indicates that water vapor in the air has changed to tiny droplets of liquid water.

  2. The weather conditions, including temperature and pressure, would have to stay the same so that the rates at which the water changes from one state to another stay the same.

51 Hot Gases

Use with Chapter 14, Section 14.1

Purpose

▶ To introduce the effect of temperature on gases

Teaching Suggestions

▶ Before projecting the transparency, blow up a balloon. Release the balloon and allow it to "fly" around the classroom. Then project the transparency, and draw attention to the exhaust coming from the rocket as it blasts off into space. Have students discuss how the balloon and rocket are similar. Lead them to recognize that the rapid expulsion of gas in one direction propels the balloon/rocket in the opposite direction. Be sure that students do not infer that the exhaust pushes against the ground to achieve liftoff.

▶ Have students answer the transparency questions and discuss their answers. You might point out that rockets generally use solid or liquid fuels, which are converted to gases when ignited and burned.

▶ *Answers to questions on the transparency include:*

  1. Flames and gases are coming out of the tail of the rocket.

  2. Accept all logical answers. One answer may be that the rocket fuel is ignited and burned, giving off a hot gas. The hot gas leaves the rocket so rapidly that the rocket is propelled in the opposite direction.

52 Getting Ready to Fly

Use with Chapter 14, Section 14.2

Purpose

▶ To illustrate the effect of temperature and pressure on the volume of a gas

Teaching Suggestions

▶ Project the transparency, and have students share their experiences of having ridden in a hot-air balloon or seeing one being flown.

▶ Show students a helium-filled balloon. Before students answer the questions, have them discuss how helium-filled balloons behave.

▶ *Answers to questions on the transparency include:*

  1. Hot-air balloons are traditionally filled with hot air.

  2. Accept all logical answers. Hot-air balloons are partially inflated by a fan and then the air is heated. When the gases are heated, the molecules of gas move more quickly and collide more frequently with the inside of the balloon, causing the balloon to become larger.

53 Delivering Energy

Use with Chapter 14, Section 14.3

Purpose

▶ To provide an example of the liquefaction of a real gas

Teaching Suggestions

▶ Project the transparency, and have students answer the questions.

▶ Have students discuss what propane, C_3H_8, is and how it is used. (Propane is a colorless, odorless gas used as fuel in homes and industries.) Allow students to share their experiences with propane.

▶ Students may think that propane has an odor. Point out that a chemical with a distinctive odor is added to propane used in homes and industries as a warning agent if a gas leak occurs.

▶ *Answers to questions on the transparency include:*

  1. Accept all logical answers. Propane gas becomes a liquid under moderate pressure and/or at lower temperatures.

  2. It is more logical to transport propane as a liquid than as a gas because the liquid takes up less room in the tanker than the gas would. This allows the transport companies to deliver more propane at one time, thus reducing the time and cost involved. Other possible issues for discussion include safety and ease of transport.

54 Making Bread

Use with Chapter 14, Section 14.4

Purpose

▶ To illustrate that amounts of reactants, including gases, and amounts of products are important in industrial processes.

Teaching Suggestions

▶ Project the transparency, and have students discuss what ingredients would be measured using various measuring utensils to make the variety of breads shown. Ingredients measured include flour, water, yeast, and possibly salt. Students should recognize that specific amounts of certain ingredients are necessary to make desired amounts of food. Point out that this same concept applies to industrial products.

▶ Have students discuss and answer the questions in small groups. Discuss how yeast in bread takes in sugar and gives off carbon dioxide gas. The carbon dioxide gas causes holes in the bread, which accounts for the bread being less dense.

▶ *Answers to questions on the transparency include:*

   1. The correct amounts of the correct ingredients are needed to make edible bread with a pleasing appearance. Variations in the amounts and types of ingredients will result in something different from the desired bread.

   2. Answers will vary, but possible responses might include that in order to make a specific industrial product, such as hydrogen peroxide, a recipe must be followed. Such a recipe is expressed as a balanced equation, where the specific number of moles of reactants (ingredients) is combined to produce a specific number of moles of product (hydrogen peroxide). Students may further conjecture that moles can be expressed as volumes of reactants producing volumes of product.

55 Solutions

Use with Chapter 15, Section 15.1

Purpose

▶ To introduce the concepts of solvent and solute

Teaching Suggestions

▶ Project the transparency, and ask students what they think the composition is of ocean water. Have students recall the definitions of heterogeneous mixture and homogeneous mixture from Chapter 3. Ask students which type of mixture describes ocean water. (Ocean water is a heterogeneous mixture because it contains bits of sand and other solid materials that can settle out of the water or can be filtered out. Ocean water is also a homogeneous mixture because it has salts and other materials dissolved in it.)

▶ Have students answer the questions on the transparency. Explain that in ocean water the water is the solvent and the salt and gases that are dissolved in the water are the solutes. Tell students that in this section they will learn more about solvents and solutes.

▶ *Answers to questions on the transparency include:*

   1. Ocean water tastes salty. When it evaporates, it leaves behind small crystals that look like table salt.

   2. Certain plants and animals live submerged in ocean water. During photosynthesis, the plants take in carbon dioxide dissolved in the water and release oxygen into the water. Both plants and animals take in oxygen dissolved in the water during cellular respiration and release carbon dioxide into the water.

56 Concentration

Use with Chapter 15, Section 15.2

Purpose

▶ To introduce the concept that concentration is expressed as a ratio

Teaching Suggestions

▶ Project the transparency, and ask students for evidence that the jar of jelly beans is a mixture. (There are several different components—colors (flavors) of jelly beans—mixed at random in a defined volume, the jar.)

▶ After students have answered the questions, ask them how they could increase their chance of selecting their favorite jelly bean. (increase the number of favorite jelly beans in the jar or decrease the number of non-favorite jelly beans in the jar) Lead students to recognize that either action would increase the concentration of favorite jelly beans in the jar. Tell students that in this section they will learn about the concentrations of solutions, including how the concentrations are expressed and how they are calculated.

▶ *Answers to questions on the transparency include:*
  1. the number of favorite jelly beans in the jar and the total number of jelly beans in the jar
  2. number of favorite jelly beans in the jar/total number of jelly beans in the jar × 100%

57 Properties of Solutions

Use with Chapter 15, Section 15.3

Purpose

▶ To illustrate the concept of freezing point depression of solutions

Teaching Suggestions

▶ Project the transparency, and ask students if they can identify the pellets. (Some students may know that the pellets are crystals of sodium chloride [halite] or potassium chloride [sylvite], two ionic compounds that are soluble in water.) Ask students where they may have seen a deicing process other than on roadways and sidewalks. (Airplane wings are deiced. You might tell students that the deicing solution used is an aqueous solution of ethylene glycol.)

▶ Use the questions on the transparency to help students recognize that the freezing point of a solution is lower than the freezing point of the pure solvent.

▶ *Answers to questions on the transparency include:*
  1. Areas around the pellets are liquid water, not ice. The solution remains as a liquid on the sidewalk, next to the frozen water.
  2. The freezing point of the aqueous pellet solution is lower than the freezing point of the pure solvent (water).

58 Heterogeneous and Homogeneous Mixtures

Use with Chapter 15, Section 15.4

Purpose

▶ To compare heterogeneous and homogeneous mixtures

Teaching Suggestions

▶ Project the transparency, and tell students that each liquid is a mixture. Have students identify the components of each mixture. (orange juice: water, sugar, natural flavoring and coloring, and pulp; apple juice: apple juice)

▶ After students have answered the questions on the transparency, ask them to classify each mixture as heterogeneous or homogeneous and to explain their reasoning. Students should recognize from Chapter 3 that the apple juice, because it has a uniform composition, is a solution, or a homogeneous mixture. The orange juice is not a solution because it has distinct parts that can separate. Thus, the orange juice is a heterogeneous mixture. Tell students that in this section they will learn about the properties of different types of heterogeneous mixtures.

▶ *Answers to questions on the transparency include:*
  1. The pulp in the orange juice has settled to the bottom of the pitcher. Stirring the orange juice will make it more evenly blended.
  2. The apple juice is evenly blended and therefore does not require stirring.

59 Heat

Use with Chapter 16, Section 16.1

Purpose

▶ To introduce the concept of heat

Teaching Suggestions

▶ Project the transparency, and direct students' attention to the fire. Relate the amount of heat produced by the fire to the size of the fire.

▶ Relate the size of the fire and the amount of heat generated to the number of trees (amount of fuel available) in the forest.

▶ Tell students that in this section they will learn what heat is and how it is measured.

▶ *Answers to questions on the transparency include:*
1. The fire is burning the trees and producing smoke.
2. Answers should refer to the concept that energy is transferred from the fire to the skin.

60 Getting Warmer
Use with Chapter 16, Section 16.2

Purpose

▶ To illustrate that the specific heat capacities of different materials affect the amount of heat given off by those materials

Teaching Suggestions

▶ Project the transparency, and direct students' attention to the warning label on the packaging. Relate the warning label to the fact that such pies are usually heated prior to sale.

▶ Lead students to recognize that the packaging will feel warm to the touch, and the piecrust will feel warmer. The pie filling will feel the warmest, possibly hot enough to cause discomfort or pain when bitten.

▶ Remind students that different materials have different specific heat capacities. Then ask students what packaging, piecrust, and pie filling are made of and how their heat capacities differ. (Packaging—paper or cardboard; piecrust—flour; pie filling—(depending on the pie) fruit, water, sugar.) Paper or cardboard has a very low specific heat capacity. Piecrust has a specific heat capacity that is somewhat greater than that of paper or cardboard and will feel slightly warmer than the packaging. Water has the highest specific heat capacity, so the heat from the pie filling will be greatest.

▶ *Answers to questions on the transparency include:*
1. The warning label states the contents may be hot.
2. The filling has a higher specific heat capacity than the crust.

61 Change in Energy
Use with Chapter 16, Section 16.3

Purpose

▶ To illustrate the impact of an endothermic process on a system

Teaching Suggestions

▶ Project the transparency, and have students describe the process of melting. (changing from solid to liquid)

▶ Remind students that a system is the part of the universe that is of interest in any process or chemical reaction. The surroundings are everything in the universe except the system. Ask students to identify the system and the surroundings in the transparency. (system: ice cream; surroundings: air and the cone)

▶ After students have answered the questions, have them speculate about the kinds of energy changes that occur when a substance changes from a liquid to a solid, a gas to liquid, and so on. Tell students that they will learn about these energy changes in this section.

▶ *Answers to questions on the transparency include:*
1. The ice cream is absorbing heat from its surroundings.
2. The ice cream is an endothermic system.

62 Heat of Reaction
Use with Chapter 16, Section 16.4

Purpose

▶ To introduce the quantitative nature of enthalpy changes

Teaching Suggestions

▶ Project the transparency, and ask students to describe how they feel when they exercise vigorously. Their answers should include that they feel hot and may sweat. Explain that this feeling comes from the heat released by the chemical reactions that take place in their muscles when they exercise.

▶ Tell students that many chemical reactions in the body are exothermic, and that the heat released by these reactions keeps the body warm. Add that working or exercising harder increases the overall rate of these reactions and thus increases the rate of heat production in the body. Explain that the evaporation of sweat absorbs heat and helps keep the body from becoming too warm.

▶ *Answers to questions on the transparency include:*
1. You can see he is exerting himself by the volume of breath that is condensing; he is breathing hard. Because he is exerting himself, his body is producing more heat than when he is at rest.
   It comes from the chemical reactions in his body.
2. His rate of heat production increases the harder he plays.

63 Increasing Disorder
Use with Chapter 16, Section 16.5

Purpose
▶ To introduce the concept of disorder

Teaching Suggestions
▶ Project the transparency, and discuss the condition of the glass and milk in each picture.

▶ Have students answer the questions and think of the situations in terms of order and disorder. Ask them to imagine a stack of magazines on a table in a doctor's office (orderly) and how those magazines would probably look by the end of the day (unstacked, spread out, some opened—disorderly).

▶ Ask students to describe other situations that show a high degree of disorder (messy room, spilled display of fruit at a grocery store, multi-vehicle accident, spreading of a fragrance, fire, fireworks, billiard balls spreading out after being hit with a cue ball, lemonade, ice cube melting).

▶ Discuss students' examples of disorder in terms of the processes and flow of energy that lead to the disorder such as bumping the display to spill the fruit, pushing of the cue stick and motion of the cue ball to hit the billiard balls, and the mixing and dissolving of a lemonade mix in water to make the lemonade.

▶ *Answers to questions on the transparency include:*
  1. The glass is broken, and the milk is spilled.
  2. The second picture shows a disorderly situation.

64 Collisions
Use with Chapter 17, Section 17.1

Purpose
▶ To introduce the concept of collisions in chemical reactions

Teaching Suggestions
▶ Project the transparency, and discuss the positions of the vehicles at the accident scene and where the vehicles are damaged.

▶ After students have answered the questions, ask students whether any of the vehicles could have been involved in more than one collision. Encourage students to provide supporting evidence. For example, students might point out that some vehicles had damage on both the front and rear or on both sides.

▶ Tell students that in this section they will read about collisions between particles that lead to chemical reactions. Have them speculate how collisions between particles may be similar to the collisions between the vehicles. (Particles may collide at varying angles and velocities.)

▶ *Answers to questions on the transparency include:*
  1. The vehicles have collided at various angles, and all the vehicles have been damaged.
  2. Some of the vehicles may be more damaged because they collided at higher velocities or at more critical angles.

65 Moving Particles
Use with Chapter 17, Section 17.2

Purpose
▶ To demonstrate the effect of temperature on the movement of particles

Teaching Suggestions
▶ Project the transparency, and lead students to recognize that the two glasses of tea differ in the temperature of the water and in the amount of tea dissolved in the water.

▶ After students have answered the questions, remind them that in Chapter 13 they learned that increasing the temperature of a substance increases the kinetic energy of its particles. Ask students how the increased energy affects the movement of the particles. (The particles move faster.)

▶ Ask students to speculate how temperature affects the number of collisions between particles and therefore the reaction rate between particles. (The higher the temperature, the faster the particles move, the more collisions there are, and the faster the reaction occurs.) Tell students that in this section they will learn about additional factors that affect reaction rates.

▶ *Answers to questions on the transparency include:*
  1. The tea particles are moving faster in the glass with hot water. The hot water is darker (has more dissolved tea) than the cold water.
  2. The particles are moving faster because the water has a higher temperature.

66 Concentration of Particles
Use with Chapter 17, Section 17.3

Purpose

▶ To introduce the effect of reactant concentration on reaction rate

Teaching Suggestions

▶ Project the transparency, and ask students to share their experiences with playing pool. They should recognize that the game requires that the balls collide in the right places and at the right speeds.

▶ After students have answered the questions, draw a connection between the concentration of balls on the table and the concentration of reactants in a chemical reaction. Have students recall from Section 17.1 that chemical reactions occur only when particles of reactants collide in favorable orientations with sufficient energy. Ask students what happens when the concentration of reactants decreases. (The number of collisions between reactant particles also decreases.) Lead students to understand that when there are fewer collisions, less energy supplied, and unfavorable orientation between reactant particles, the reaction rate decreases.

▶ *Answers to questions on the transparency include:*

1. The cue ball will move forward and collide with one or more of the other balls. As those balls move, they may collide with other balls.
2. Decreasing the number of balls will probably result in fewer collisions between the balls.

67 Following the Steps
Use with Chapter 17, Section 17.4

Purpose

▶ To introduce the concept of reaction mechanism

Teaching Suggestions

▶ Project the transparency, and discuss students' experiences with recipes in baking and cooking. Then have them answer the questions.

▶ Ask students if they know of any recipes in which some of the steps take longer to complete than others. Tell them that many chemical reactions also take place in a sequence of steps in which some steps take longer than others. The sequence of steps is called a reaction mechanism.

▶ *Answers to questions on the transparency include:*

1. A recipe is a sequence of steps for making a food product.
2. The finished product is not likely to be the expected or desired result.

68 Equilibrium: A State of Dynamic Balance
Use with Chapter 18, Section 18.1

Purpose

▶ To introduce the concept of chemical equilibrium as being a state of stability but not a situation where the forward and the reverse reaction occur at equal rates

Teaching Suggestions

▶ Project the transparency, and ask students to identify what the person in the boat is attempting to do.

▶ After students have made their suggestions, ask them if the person has to remove all the water to keep the boat afloat. Tell students that many chemical reactions reach a state of balance, or stability, but that this does not necessarily mean that all reactants have been converted to product. Emphasize that just because a reaction may not run to completion (just because the person can't bail all the water out of the boat) it doesn't mean that the reaction hasn't reached a state of stability.

▶ Explain that many chemical reactions run in both the forward and reverse directions. Again, direct students' attention to the transparency. Ask them what would be the "forward" and "reverse" reactions in this case. Elicit an understanding that, at any point, the boat could become "stable." All the person has to do is remove water at the same rate the leak is allowing the water in the boat.

▶ Tell students that in this section they will learn about chemical equilibrium.

▶ *Answers to questions on the transparency include:*

1. To keep the boat from sinking any lower, the man has to remove water at the same rate the leak is allowing the water in the boat.
2. If the man began removing water more quickly, the boat would rise a little higher. The man would be removing the water more quickly than the water is coming in the boat. If the man began removing water more slowly, the boat would sink lower because water is coming in faster than it is being removed.

69 Factors Affecting Chemical Equilibrium

Use with Chapter 18, Section 18.2

Purpose

▶ To introduce Le Châtelier's principle by showing how objects react to stresses such as changes in heat and pressure

Teaching Suggestions

▶ Project the transparency, and ask students to describe the physical state of the can.

▶ After students have made suggestions, explain how heat can crumple the can. Water inside the sealed can turns into steam when heated. When the steam condenses, it lowers the air pressure inside the can. The air pressure outside is then greater and thus crushes the can.

▶ Tell students that in this section they will learn how Le Châtelier's principle will help them determine how stresses such as changes in pressure, temperature, and concentration affect chemical equilibrium.

▶ *Answers to questions on the transparency include:*
   1. The can might be described as crumpled, bent, or buckled.
   2. Students might suggest that the can buckled from partial melting by heat, or that it was crushed by hand or in a vice. Some students might surmise that the can buckled because of a partial vacuum inside. The sealed can had a little water inside it and when the can was heated, the water turned to steam. The can was then cooled and the steam condensed. When it condensed, the air pressure inside the can became lower and thus the outside air pressure was able to crush the can.

70 Using Equilibrium Constants

Use with Chapter 18, Section 18.3

Purpose

▶ To introduce the concept of determining the extent of solubility and how various factors might affect equilibrium

Teaching Suggestions

▶ Project the transparency, and ask students to identify what is happening in the pictures.

▶ Explain that fudge is a mixture of butter, milk, sugar, and chocolate, and that when it cools, the sugar crystallizes to give the fudge its consistency. Ask students if they know of any factors that might limit the amount of sugar that the fudge could contain. Offer other examples of solutions, such as lemonade and tea, to stimulate thinking. Lead students to recognize that changes in temperature and pressure can affect the rate and the extent of solubility just as these changes can affect the equilibrium of a chemical reaction.

▶ Tell students that in this section they will learn how they can use equilibrium expressions to study solutions.

▶ *Answers to questions on the transparency include:*
   1. The fudge has cooled.
   2. To make the fudge harder, you could add more sugar. To make the fudge softer, you could add more milk. In each case, you are pushing the equilibrium of the solution in a different direction.

71 Properties of Acids and Bases

Use with Chapter 19, Section 19.1

Purpose

▶ To introduce the properties of acids and bases

Teaching Suggestions

▶ Project the transparency, and point out that the acids and bases studied in this chapter have properties that can be used to identify them.

▶ List answers to question 2 and review after the properties of acids and bases are discussed in this section. Caution students to never taste or feel anything in the laboratory unless directed to do so.

▶ Students probably consider acids to be dangerous. Point out that some acids are dangerous for human contact, but others are commonly found in foods.

▶ Ask students to identify some bases (baking soda, milk of magnesia, soap) and to describe some of their characteristics.

▶ *Answers to questions on the transparency include:*
   1. slippery
   2. Students might list such properties as reactivity and taste.

72 Strengths of Acids
Use with Chapter 19, Section 19.2

Purpose

▶ To introduce the concept of strong and weak acids

Teaching Suggestions

▶ Project the transparency, and ask students how many have used eyedrops. Elicit from students that the drops were soothing to the eye.

▶ Bring samples of several different eyedrops to class and compare their ingredients. Have students identify any acids present.

▶ Tell students that in this section they will read about the strengths of acids and bases. Emphasize the point that because an acid may be weak, it does not imply that the acid is dilute.

▶ *Answers to questions on the transparency include:*

   1. Boric acid is weak; the acidity in the drops is similar to that of the fluids in the human eye. Some students may speculate that boric acid is not very reactive and thus not harmful to human tissue.

   2. Hydrochloric, sulfuric, and nitric acids might be mentioned because they are reactive with human tissue.

73 Measuring Acidity
Use with Chapter 19, Section 19.3

Purpose

▶ To introduce measuring acidity by pH

Teaching Suggestions

▶ Project the transparency, and ask students how many have tested pool water or have seen it done. If any have pool-testing experience, ask them to describe what the testing determines.

▶ Bring a pool-testing kit to class and examine the contents and procedure for testing the water.

▶ Ask students to share examples of what happens to pool water that contains the wrong balance of additives. Students might mention unwanted growth of algae or other microorganisms.

▶ Tell students that in this section they will learn how the acidity of substances, such as that of pool water, is measured.

▶ *Answers to questions on the transparency include:*

   1. The water is being tested to be sure it contains the correct amounts of chemicals that keep the water clean and safe for swimming. Students may also know that the water is tested for levels of microorganisms.

   2. Microorganisms might grow or the water itself might harm human tissue.

74 Neutralizing Soil
Use with Chapter 19, Section 19.4

Purpose

▶ To introduce the concept of acid-base neutralization

Teaching Suggestions

▶ Project the transparency, and ask students what they know about the importance of the pH of soil. Encourage them to share their answers.

▶ Tell students that certain plants grow best in acidic soil, and others grow best in soil that is slightly basic. Many plants will not grow in soil that is noticeably acidic or basic. Students might want to gather more information about this topic from a local greenhouse or horticulture expert.

▶ Ask students to hypothesize how soil might become acidic. One of the most common reasons is acid rain, which can be common around industrialized areas.

▶ Tell students that lime is also added to lakes that have become acidic to bring the pH of the water to a level that is healthy for organisms growing there.

▶ Ask students to predict the results if they tested the pH of their local soil. If possible, have students test their predictions in the laboratory.

▶ *Answers to questions on the transparency include:*

   1. Lime must be a base that reacts with the acid in the soil.

   2. The soil might become too basic and certain types of plants would not grow.

75 Bleaching

Use with Chapter 20, Section 20.1

Purpose

▶ To introduce a common oxidation–reduction reaction

Teaching Suggestions

▶ Project the transparency, and ask students to share similar experiences. How many have had a favorite item of clothing ruined by chlorine bleach? Ask students for what purpose bleach is used on fabrics. (to whiten and disinfect certain kinds of white fabrics)

▶ Have students compare care labels in items of clothing and note similarities in the fabrics of those whose labels specify that no bleach should be used.

▶ Elicit from students that the use of bleach involves a chemical reaction. Tell students that this chapter introduces a way to classify reactions that differs from the classification system used in Chapter 10.

▶ *Answers to questions on the transparency include*:
   1. The bleach causes the fabric to whiten.
   2. The stain or dye on the fabric undergoes a chemical reaction with the bleach.

76 Balancing Numbers

Use with Chapter 20, Section 20.2

Purpose

▶ To introduce the concept that adding electrons lowers the oxidation number of an element and losing electrons raises it.

Teaching Suggestions

▶ Review with students the rules of adding and subtracting signed numbers.

▶ Project the transparency, and use a number line to help students with the questions. Students should think of the amount owed as a positive amount and the amount paid back as a negative amount. For question 2, the additional amount borrowed also is a positive amount.

▶ For clarification, have students write problems relating to the loan situation using real numbers. Have students discuss their answers.

▶ Tell students that in this section they will learn how adding and losing electrons affect an element's oxidation number. Use the transparency as an analogy for explaining changes in oxidation numbers.

▶ *Answers to questions on the transparency include:*
   1. The total amount owed becomes less.
   2. The total amount owed becomes greater.

77 Giving and Taking

Use with Chapter 20, Section 20.3

Purpose

▶ To introduce the concept that many events are actually two actions occurring at once, leading into the transferring of electrons from one atom or ion to another

Teaching Suggestions

▶ Project the transparency, and have students discuss their answers to question 1.

▶ Make two columns on the chalkboard. Label one column "Giving" and the other "Taking." As students provide answers to question 2, have them state the separate actions that occur simultaneously. For example, if a student's answer is the giving of a gift to someone, the column items would indicate that one person is taking the gift at the same time the other person is giving it. Emphasize that both columns represent the same event; they are just different points of view.

▶ *Answers to questions on the transparency include:*
   1. Both actions are occurring simultaneously.
   2. Accept any reasonable answer. Possible answers include giving a gift, passing a football, and shaking hands.

78 Voltaic Cells

Use with Chapter 21, Section 21.1

Purpose

▶ To introduce the properties and usefulness of voltaic cells

Teaching Suggestions

▶ Project the transparency, and call students' attention to the batteries under the hood of the car. Make sure students understand that this car has no internal combustion engine and does not run on gasoline. Instead, the car is powered by an electric motor that uses the energy stored in the batteries. Add that batteries are also called voltaic cells.

▶ Ask students to recall what they learned about redox reactions in Chapter 20. Remind them that all redox reactions involve a transfer of electrons. Tell students that batteries contain chemicals that undergo redox reactions, but the electrons that are transferred flow through a circuit outside the battery. Explain that this flow of electrons can be used to power electric devices, such as electric cars.

▶ *Answers to questions on the transparency include:*

  1. Electric energy makes the car run.

  2. The energy comes from batteries.

79 Corrosion

Use with Chapter 21, Section 21.2

Purpose

▶ To illustrate corrosion

Teaching Suggestions

▶ Project the transparency, and ask students to examine the ship for signs of corrosion, or rusting. Places where corrosion has occurred should look orange or brown. Ask students if corrosion appears to have happened more extensively on one part of the ship than on others. It should be obvious that the part of the hull that is normally submerged is the most corroded.

▶ Explain that corrosion is the result of a naturally occurring voltaic cell in which metallic iron gives up electrons to become Fe^{3+} ions, which combine with oxygen to form iron(III) oxide, commonly called rust. Remind students that in all voltaic cells, electrolytes must be able to move between the anode and the cathode. Add that water provides a medium through which electrolytes can move in this reaction, which explains why corrosion is more extensive on parts of a boat that are normally submerged.

▶ *Answers to questions on the transparency include:*

  1. Exposure to oxygen and contact with water have caused the rusting of iron on the ship.

  2. The iron is undergoing oxidation.

80 Electroplating

Use with Chapter 21, Section 21.3

Purpose

▶ To illustrate electroplating

Teaching Suggestions

▶ Project the transparency, and make sure students understand what it illustrates. Explain that it shows an electrochemical cell in which chromium ions are being reduced to metallic chromium, which is deposited on these steel auto parts. Ask students whether the auto parts are anodes or cathodes. (cathodes) Remind students that steel is an iron alloy and that chromium is a self-protecting metal, like aluminum and zinc.

▶ Tell students that chromium has a lower standard reduction potential than iron. With this information, students should realize that in an iron-chromium cell, the spontaneous reaction would result in the *oxidation* of chromium. Remind them that a spontaneous reaction in an electrochemical cell produces electric current. Explain that to make an iron-chromium cell *reduce* chromium, the spontaneous reaction must be reversed, and that can be done by supplying electric current to the cell in the opposite direction.

▶ *Answers to questions on the transparency include:*

  1. The auto parts are being plated with chromium to protect them from corrosion and to make them shiny.

  2. The reaction is not spontaneous.

81 Organic and Inorganic Compounds

Use with Chapter 22, Section 22.1

Purpose

▶ To compare organic and inorganic compounds

Teaching Suggestions

▶ Project the transparency, and ask students to think about the first question. Have them consider everything they can see in the photograph, including all of the parts of the grill (lid, window, bottom, shelves, handles, control knobs, tank, hose, wheels), the shish kebab skewers, the food, the plate, and the plastic wrap. After students have proposed their answers, explain that almost all carbon-containing compounds are classified as organic compounds. Emphasize that organic compounds are found not just in things that are or once were living, but also in a variety of other substances, such as plastics, rubber, and petroleum products. Allow students to reconsider their answers.

▶ Tell students that the gas this barbecue grill burns is called propane, and that propane belongs to a class of organic compounds known as hydrocarbons, which are the subject of the chapter.

▶ *Answers to questions on the transparency include:*

1. Items that contain organic compounds include all of the food, the plastic plates, the various wooden or plastic parts of the barbecue grill (shelf, handles, hose, wheels), and the gas in the tank. Entirely inorganic items include all metal parts of the grill (lid, bottom, tank), glassware, and table top.

2. The grill produces heat by burning the gas propane, an organic compound that is stored in the tank.

82 Properties of Methane
Use with Chapter 22, Section 22.2

Purpose

▶ To introduce the physical properties of alkanes

Teaching Suggestions

▶ Project the transparency, and explain that certain kinds of bacteria that live in the bottom of marshes and swamps produce methane from carbon dioxide and hydrogen. The methane rises out of the water and, if the air is still, may form a hazy cloud that hovers over the surface of the marsh. Tell students that methane formed in this way is known as marsh gas or swamp gas.

▶ Ask students what they can infer about the relative boiling points of methane and water if methane bubbles out of the water in a marsh. (Methane has a lower boiling point than water.) Then ask students to compare the structural formulas and molecular masses of methane (CH_4, 16 amu) and water H_2O, 18 amu). Have students think about why two molecules that are so similar in size and mass should have different physical properties. They should recall that a molecule's physical properties are influenced by the strength of intermolecular attraction, which depends on the polarity of bonds in the molecule. Tell students that in this section they will explore this idea in more detail.

▶ *Answers to questions on the transparency include:*
1. the bubbles
2. Methane is a gas at the temperatures normally found in swamps.

83 Unsaturated Hydrocarbons
Use with Chapter 22, Section 22.3

Purpose

▶ To introduce alkenes and alkynes

Teaching Suggestions

▶ Project the transparency, and direct students to examine the chemical structure carefully. If they have difficulty identifying what is wrong with the structure, ask them to recall the electronic configurations of carbon and hydrogen. Remind them that these configurations determine the number of covalent bonds that each atom can form.

▶ As students propose ways to revise the structure, they should recognize that one of the revisions, $H_3C—CH_3$, represents the saturated hydrocarbon ethane (C_2H_6). Point out that the other two correct revisions, $H_2C=CH_2$ and $HC\equiv CH$, represent unsaturated hydrocarbons, which they will learn about in this section. To help students remember the distinction between saturated and unsaturated hydrocarbons, draw an analogy between a saturated sponge, which holds as much water as it can, and a saturated hydrocarbon such as ethane, in which the carbon atoms "hold" as many hydrogen atoms as they can with only single bonds.

▶ *Answers to questions on the transparency include:*
1. A carbon atom can make only four bonds, but each carbon in the structure on the transparency makes five bonds.
2. There are three ways to make the structure correct: change the double bond to a single bond, forming ethane; remove one hydrogen from each carbon and leave the double bond; or remove two hydrogens from each carbon and change the double bond to a triple bond.

84 Optical Isomers
Use with Chapter 22, Section 22.4

Purpose

▶ To introduce the concept of isomers

Teaching Suggestions

▶ Project the transparency, and have students try to imagine rotating one of the gloves so that it is indistinguishable from the other. If they have difficulty performing this task mentally, they can use their own hands instead. They should quickly realize that the gloves, like their hands, cannot be rotated to look the same. Each glove is a mirror image of the other.

▶ Point out that certain pairs of organic compounds also exist as mirror images, and that such pairs are called optical isomers. Explain that, like right-handed and left-handed gloves, the two compounds in a pair of optical isomers have very similar properties but differ in the way their parts are arranged in space. Tell students that in this section they will learn more about optical and other kinds of isomers.

▶ *Answers to questions on the transparency include:*
 1. Answers may vary. Similarities include the style, composition, color, and size of the gloves. The difference is that one glove is right-handed and the other is left-handed.
 2. No, the gloves cannot be rotated so they look the same.

85 Petroleum
Use with Chapter 22, Section 22.5
Purpose
▶ To introduce the extraction and uses of petroleum

Teaching Suggestions
▶ Project the transparency as you describe the process of extracting petroleum. Tell students that an oil-drilling rig extends a series of connected, rotating pipes down through the ground to a petroleum reservoir. A drill bit on the lowest pipe can cut through even the hardest rock. When the pipe reaches the reservoir, the petroleum, which is under high pressure, flows up through the pipe to the surface.

▶ Explain that petroleum is a mixture of many organic compounds, and that to be useful it must be separated into its components. Point out that petroleum is the main source of the hydrocarbons used in industry.

▶ *Answers to questions on the transparency include:*
 1. Oil companies drill through Earth's crust into reservoirs that contain petroleum, and the petroleum flows or is pumped to the surface.
 2. Petroleum is used to make gasoline and other fuels, solvents, lubricants, tar, asphalt, plastics, and many other organic compounds.

86 A Source of Many Materials
Use with Chapter 23, Section 23.1
Purpose
▶ To introduce the idea that carbon is the basis of a wide variety of materials

Teaching Suggestions
▶ Project the transparency, and have students answer the questions. Ask them to name other useful carbon-based materials. (Examples include paper, wood, polyester, and nylon.)

▶ Point out that the materials in the photographs are not made up of hydrocarbons, but of compounds called substituted hydrocarbons that contain other elements along with carbon and hydrogen. Tell students that Chapter 23 discusses such compounds.

▶ *Answers to questions on the transparency include:*
 1. Charcoal briquettes are shown. They are made up almost completely of the element carbon.
 2. The materials include Teflon (pan), PVC (piping), and plastic food wrap.

87 A Useful Organic Liquid
Use with Chapter 23, Section 23.2
Purpose
▶ To introduce the class of substituted hydrocarbons known as alcohols

Teaching Suggestions
▶ Project the transparency, and draw attention to the label on the bottle. Ask students if they have ever had their skin swabbed in this way before being given an injection.

▶ After students have answered the questions, point out that the chemical name for ethyl alcohol is ethanol. Explain to students that alcohols are one class of substituted hydrocarbons, which they will read about in this section. In addition to containing carbon and hydrogen, an alcohol molecule also contains oxygen.

▶ *Answers to questions on the transparency include:*
 1. The liquid, ethyl alcohol, is being used to disinfect the skin before an injection is given.
 2. Answers will vary. Properties might include color-lessness, low boiling point, tendency to evaporate

readily (volatility), and characteristic odor. Ethyl alcohol is used to make alcoholic beverages, as a solvent in varnishes and stains, and as a gasoline additive.

88 A Powerful Solvent

Use with Chapter 23, Section 23.3

Purpose

▶ To introduce the class of compounds called esters

Teaching Suggestions

▶ Before projecting the transparency, point out that substituted hydrocarbons have an enormous range of uses that depend on their properties, which result from their characteristic functional groups.

▶ After projecting the transparency and discussing the answers to the questions, explain that the main active ingredient in many nail polish removers is ethyl acetate. Ethyl acetate belongs to a class of substituted hydrocarbons called esters.

▶ *Answers to questions on the transparency include:*
  1. Nail polish remover takes off nail polish by dissolving it.
  2. Nail polish remover must be a good solvent for materials, such as oil-based paints in nail polish, that are not very soluble in water.

89 Saturated and Unsaturated Fats

Use with Chapter 23, Section 23.4

Purpose

▶ To contrast the properties of saturated and unsaturated fats

Teaching Suggestions

▶ Project the transparency, and ask students which of the fats they use at home. Then have students answer the questions.

▶ Students probably have heard or read about saturated and unsaturated fats. Ask them which fats in the photograph they think are unsaturated and which are saturated. (Fats that are hard at room temperature, such as lard and butter, are saturated, whereas softer fats, such as easy-spread margarine and oils, are not.) You may

wish to discuss the health benefits of eating unsaturated fats instead of saturated fats.

▶ Tell students that in this section they will learn about the chemical difference between saturated and unsaturated fats and the chemical reactions that produce the two kinds of fats.

▶ *Answers to questions on the transparency include:*
  1. The lard, butter, and margarine are solids, although the margarine is softer than the lard and butter. The olive oil is a liquid.
  2. Because the olive oil is a liquid at room temperature, its melting point must be lower than room temperature. Because the other fats are solid at room temperature, their melting points must be higher than room temperature.

90 Polymers

Use with Chapter 23, Section 23.5

Purpose

▶ To introduce some synthetic polymers and their properties

Teaching Suggestions

▶ Project the transparency, and ask students to identify the objects they see, focusing on the materials from which the objects are made.

▶ After students have answered the questions, tell them that the materials shown are made up of very large carbon-containing compounds called polymers.

▶ Discuss how the properties of polymers determine their uses. For example, flexible plastics are used to make food wraps, bags, and squeeze bottles.

▶ Tell students that in this section they will learn about the structure of synthetic polymers and the reactions by which these polymers are made.

▶ *Answers to questions on the transparency include:*
  1. All the objects are made of synthetic materials, including plastics and nylon.
  2. The objects vary in hardness, flexibility, thickness, transparency, and ability to insulate against heat loss.

91 Protein Polymers
Use with Chapter 24, Section 24.1

Purpose

▶ To introduce proteins

Teaching Suggestions

▶ Project the transparency, and explain that all of the substances shown are made of polymers. Tell students that some polymers occur naturally and some are synthetic.

▶ Point out that the synthetic and natural polymers have similar properties. They all are lightweight but strong. As a result, the cocoon and the feather can provide protection from the environment. The bodies of animals produce these polymers. Ask students to speculate on what the main building block of these polymers might be.

▶ *Answers to questions on the transparency include:*
  1. Nylon thread is lightweight but strong. It is somewhat elastic.
  2. Nylon is synthetic, and the other polymers are natural. The polymers that make up feathers and cocoons are proteins; nylon is not a protein polymer.

92 Carbohydrates
Use with Chapter 24, Section 24.2

Purpose

▶ To compare different kinds of carbohydrates

Teaching Suggestions

▶ Project the transparency, and explain that table sugar is composed entirely of sucrose. Point out that each sucrose molecule is made up of two smaller molecules—glucose and fructose.

▶ Explain that potatoes are made mostly of starch, and corncobs are made of cellulose. These substances are polymers of just one kind of subunit, glucose. Ask students to think about how potatoes and corncobs can have such different consistencies even though their major constituents are built from the same kind of subunit. Tell them that the difference lies in the way the glucose subunits are linked.

▶ *Answers to questions on the transparency include:*
  1. Humans can use the sucrose and starch as food.
  2. Humans cannot use corncobs for food because they cannot digest cellulose.

93 Lipids
Use with Chapter 24, Section 24.3

Purpose

▶ To introduce some properties of lipids

Teaching Suggestions

▶ Project the transparency, and tell students that vegetable oil and shortening are both forms of lipid.

▶ Point out that many lipid molecules have hydrocarbon chains that may be saturated or unsaturated. Ask students to recall the difference between saturated and unsaturated hydrocarbons. (Saturated—all carbon atoms connected by single bonds; unsaturated—at least one double or triple bond between carbon atoms) Explain that hydrogenation (adding hydrogen atoms) converts unsaturated hydrocarbons to saturated hydrocarbons and affects some of the properties of lipids, including melting point.

▶ *Answers to questions on the transparency include:*
  1. They are both lipids; they are insoluble in water; they store energy. One is a liquid, and one is a solid at room temperature.
  2. Hydrogenation raises the melting point.

94 DNA
Use with Chapter 24, Section 24.4

Purpose

▶ To introduce DNA

Teaching Suggestions

▶ Project the transparency, and tell students that the dark-colored bands in the photograph represent fragments of DNA. Note that the fragments have been treated with a dye that makes them visible in ultraviolet light. Explain that DNA is a large organic polymer that stores and transmits genetic information in all organisms.

▶ Ask students what they have heard or read about DNA in recent news reports. Topics might include the Human Genome Project; foods made from genetically modified organisms; medicines produced through recombinant-DNA techniques; the analysis of DNA sequences to solve crimes, identify bodies, or establish paternity; and attempts to treat inherited diseases through gene therapy.

▶ *Answers to questions on the transparency include:*

1. A person's fingerprints are unique, and so is a person's DNA.

2. Answers may vary. When police find hair, blood, or other tissue samples at a crime scene, they can analyze the DNA in the sample and compare it to the DNA of a suspect. If the suspect's DNA matches the DNA in the sample, it is very likely that the suspect was at the crime scene.

95 Metabolism

Use with Chapter 24, Section 24.5

Purpose

▶ To introduce basic concepts of metabolism

Teaching Suggestions

▶ Project the transparency, and tell students that organisms carry out thousands of different chemical reactions in their bodies and that these reactions are referred to collectively as metabolism. Explain that metabolism requires two things: energy, which allows nonspontaneous reactions to occur; and chemical building blocks, from which larger organic molecules can be synthesized.

▶ Ask students where the energy that enters living things ultimately comes from. (mostly from the Sun) Point out that some organisms can obtain energy directly from the Sun, and that when they are eaten, some of that energy is passed along to the organisms that eat them.

▶ *Answers to questions on the transparency include:*

1. Plants obtain energy from sunlight through photosynthesis and use this energy to make chemical building blocks from inorganic molecules.

2. Animals obtain energy and chemical building blocks by eating other organisms.

96 Medical Uses of Nuclear Radiation

Use with Chapter 25, Section 25.1

Purpose

▶ To introduce the use of nuclear radiation in the treatment of diseases

Teaching Suggestions

▶ Project the transparency, and ask students to discuss any experiences they have had with the use of nuclear radiation in treating diseases.

▶ Ask students if they know of any other ways in which radiation is used in medicine. For example, radiation is used to produce X rays for the diagnosis of medical and dental conditions.

▶ Draw from students any information they may know about the possible risks of being exposed to radiation.

▶ *Answers to questions on the transparency include:*

1. Student responses may vary, depending on the extent of their previous experience with radiation as a method for treating diseases. In the photo, nuclear radiation is being used to kill a patient's cancer cells.

2. Student responses may vary, depending on the extent of their previous experience with radiation. However, many students may know that radiation kills healthy tissue as well as diseased tissue, which can lead to the patient experiencing detrimental side effects and serious complications.

97 Instability

Use with Chapter 25, Section 25.2

Purpose

▶ To introduce the concept of nuclear instability

Teaching Suggestions

▶ Project the transparency, and use the photo to talk about the concept of instability.

▶ After students have answered the questions, ask them to draw parallels between the instability of a rock formation and the instability of an atomic nucleus. Have them point out how the methods and timing by which a rock formation reaches stability can be applied to an atomic nucleus.

▶ *Answers to questions on the transparency include*:

1. The rock formation is unstable because it is unlikely to remain in its present configuration for a long period of time.
2. The rock formation will become stable when broken apart and/or after it falls down, although precisely when that event will occur is not known.

98 Chemical Change or Nuclear Change?
Use with Chapter 25, Section 25.3

Purpose
▶ To compare and contrast chemical changes and nuclear changes

Teaching Suggestions
▶ Project the transparency, and have students answer the first question. Ask them to identify the type of chemical change shown. (combustion)

▶ Have students recall from Section 25.1 what happens during a nuclear change. Then have them answer the second question. You might want to list on the chalkboard all the differences and similarities between nuclear and chemical changes that students identify. As a class, review the accuracy of the list and make any necessary changes.

▶ After students have answered the questions, tell them that in this section they will learn how scientists have produced new kinds of elements by artificially producing nuclear changes in existing elements.

▶ *Answers to questions on the transparency include*:
1. chemical change
2. Both nuclear changes and chemical changes involve energy and result in a substance changing into a different substance. Chemical changes involve the electrons of atoms. Nuclear changes involve the nuclei of atoms and release radiation.

99 Nuclear Reactions and Energy
Use with Chapter 25, Section 25.4

Purpose
▶ To introduce nuclear fission and nuclear fusion

Teaching Suggestions
▶ Project the transparency, and ask students if they know what produced the mushroom-shaped cloud in the photo. (the explosion of a nuclear weapon on or immediately below Earth's surface) Explain to students that during a nuclear explosion, a huge fireball is produced that rises from Earth's surface and sucks up a column of dust from the surface, forming a so-called mushroom cloud.

▶ Ask students to think about the kinds of energy produced by a nuclear explosion and by the Sun.

▶ After students have answered the questions, explain that nuclear reactions are the source of the Sun's energy as well as the energy of a nuclear explosion. However, the kind of nuclear reaction that occurs is different in each case. Tell students that in this section they will read about the two kinds of nuclear reactions, called nuclear fission and nuclear fusion.

▶ *Answers to questions on the transparency include:*
1. Both the Sun and a nuclear explosion produce large amounts of heat, light, and other forms of electromagnetic radiation, such as gamma rays. Some students may know that both are the result of nuclear reactions.
2. A nuclear explosion may produce sound and a cloud of dust, as shown in the photo. The energy of a nuclear explosion is more short-term than the Sun's energy. Some students may know that a nuclear explosion is produced by nuclear fission and that the energy in the Sun is produced by nuclear fusion.

100 Using Radioisotopes
Use with Chapter 25, Section 25.5

Purpose
▶ To illustrate the detection and introduce the uses of radioisotopes

Teaching Suggestions

▶ Project the transparency, and point out that the device shown is called a Geiger counter, which detects radiation through the use of ionizing radiation. Point out that the man in the photo is measuring low-level radioactive waste and that he would be dressed in more protective gear if measuring higher-level waste.

▶ Remind students that in Section 25.1 they learned that a radioisotope is an isotope of an atom with an unstable nucleus that emits radiation to become more stable. Then explain that the detection of radioisotopes has many uses in industry, research, and medicine. Introduce students to a couple of industrial uses. For example, radioisotopes are added to oil in a pipeline so as to track the flow of the oil. Radioisotopes also are used to measure and control the thickness of materials produced in sheets, such as paper and steel. A source of radioisotopes is positioned on one side of the sheet material with a detector on the other side. The detector measures the amount of radiation that gets through, which indicates the thickness of the material. The detector can then adjust the rollers of the machinery to keep the material at the desired thickness.

▶ *Answers to questions on the transparency include:*
   1. gamma rays
   2. He is measuring radiation from radioactive waste. Some students may know that he is using a Geiger counter.

101 Effects of Changes in Earth's Atmosphere
Use with Chapter 26, Section 26.1

Purpose

▶ To introduce the concept that chemical changes in the atmosphere can have far-reaching effects

Teaching Suggestions

▶ Project the transparency and have students make conjectures about how pollution could have damaged the trees.

▶ These trees are located in the Czech Republic. Point out this location on a map, and discuss the proximity to large urban and industrial areas and the power plants needed to provide energy for these areas. Discuss how weather patterns might affect the movement of air pollution from one place to another.

▶ Let students speculate and discuss the kind of pollution that damaged the trees (acid rain). If students mention acid rain in their discussion, find out what they know about this type of pollution including its sources, the chemical reactions involved, and their effects on living things.

▶ *Answers to questions on the transparency include:*
   1. Pollution can travel great distances from its source by way of wind and water currents.
   2. Acid rain, a type of air pollution, damaged the trees.

102 Uses of Freshwater
Use with Chapter 26, Section 26.2

Purpose

▶ To encourage students to think about the ways in which they use, and possibly waste, water

Teaching Suggestions

▶ Project the transparency and have students name all of the uses of water shown. Discuss and list other uses of freshwater not shown on the transparency.

▶ Discuss the source of your community's drinking water and how it is treated.

▶ Record students' answers about how much water they think they use for each purpose shown. You might want to broaden the categories shown in the transparency. For example, watering plants can also include watering the yard. Washing the car can also include water used for housecleaning, and washing your face and hands can also include bathing. Compare students' answers to the volumes given in the section on page 852. Discuss ways students might conserve water.

▶ Have students describe what happens to the water after it has been used in each way shown and how its use changes the quality of the water.

▶ *Answers to questions on the transparency include:*
   1. for watering plants and for washing cars and people
   2. Answers will vary, but students are likely to underestimate the amounts.

103 Mineral Resources
Use with Chapter 26, Section 26.3

Purpose

▶ To introduce students to the practical uses of Earth's mineral resources

Teaching Suggestions

▶ Project the transparency and have students describe what it shows. The photograph shows an open pit copper mine in Brazil.

▶ Explain that open pit mining is one method of mining that is used when ore deposits lie in hard rock at or near Earth's surface. Open pit mining is a relatively inexpensive way to recover metals such as copper and iron, diamonds, phosphate, and gypsum. A shaft mine is used to recover ores from deep beneath Earth's surface. In shaft mining, miners dig a shaft 2700 meters or more deep and remove the ores through a network of horizontal passageways. Construction of shaft mines is expensive. As a result, it is used chiefly to mine the ores of valuable metals such as copper, gold, lead, silver, and zinc.

▶ Discuss how an open pit mine differs from a shaft mine and why one method might be favored over another depending on the depth of the ore deposits, how they are situated, the geography of the landscape, and cost.

▶ Encourage student to infer why the mine consists of concentric circles (to reach different levels of the mine).

▶ Have students name mineral resources that they may know are mined by this process.

▶ Discuss the benefits and risks of open pit mining to society.

▶ *Answers to questions on the transparency include:*
  1. The photograph shows open pit mining.
  2. Open pit mining can result in erosion of land, loss of plant and animal life, and water pollution due to the runoff of rainwater. It may also destroy the natural beauty of an area.

104 Earth as a Greenhouse
Use with Chapter 26, Section 26.4

Purpose

▶ To introduce the concept of the greenhouse effect in Earth's atmosphere

Teaching Suggestions

▶ Project the transparency and ask students to describe the conditions inside a greenhouse. Identify the specific conditions that are different inside and outside the greenhouse.

▶ Have students hypothesize why a greenhouse is able to stay warm in the winter. Ask students to speculate what surrounds Earth that keeps heat from escaping but also lets in solar energy.

▶ *Answers to questions on the transparency include:*
  1. The temperature and humidity are much higher than outside.
  2. Glass lets in light and heat and holds in heat.

CREDITS

Art Credits
MacArt Design: **12, 43, 68;** Navta Associates: **16, 21**

Photo Credits
1 David Kelly Crow/PhotoEdit; **2** AP/Wide World Photos; **3** Holt Studios/Nigel Cattlin/Photo Researchers; **4** David Woodfall/Stone; **5** Jean Marc Barey/Photo Researchers; **6** John Lei/Stock Boston; **7** Tom Pantages; **8** Tony Freeman/PhotoEdit; **9** (tl)Adrienne Hart-Davis/Photo Researchers, (tr)Corbis, (b)Michael Newman/PhotoEdit; **10** (l)Mark Kelley/Stone, (r)Wayne R. Bilenduke/Stone; **11** (l)Tom Pantages, (tr)Tom Pantages, (br)Eyewire Collection; **13** (tl)Paolo Koch/Photo Researchers, (tr)Breck P. Kent/Earth Scenes, (br)Tom McHugh/Photo Researchers; **14** (l)Burke & Triolo/Artville/PictureQuest (PNI), (r)C. Behr/Lone Wolf Arts; **15** (t)Charles D. Winters/Photo Researchers, (b)Richard Megna/Fundamental Photographs; **17** George Hunter/Stone; **18** Jordan Harris/PhotoEdit; **19** Richard Pasley/Stock Boston; **20** Klaus Rose/Okapia/Photo Researchers; **21** (l)Jeff Lepore/Photo Researchers, (r)Michael P. Gadomski/Photo Researchers, (b)E. R. Degginger/Photo Researchers; **22** Brian Bahr/AllSport USA; **23** Tom Pantages; **24** Raymond Gendreau/Stone; **25** (tl)courtesy of American Numismatic Society, (br)courtesy of American Numismatic Society; **26** Stephen Frisch/Stock Boston; **27** David Young-Wolff/PhotoEdit; **28** Michael Newman/PhotoEdit; **29** Earl Kowall/Corbis; **30** Charles D. Winters/Photo Researchers; **31** (tl)Vic Bider/PhotoEdit, (tr)Jeff Rotman/Stone, (bl)Tony Freeman/PhotoEdit, (br)Tom Pantages; **32** Rick Friedman/BlackStar/PictureQuest (PNI); **33** Tom Pantages; **34** Arthur Tilley/FPG; **35** Michael Newman/PhotoEdit; **36** (tl)Stephen Frisch/Stock Boston, (tr)James L. Amos/Photo Researchers; (b)Michael Dalton/Fundamental Photographs; **37** Richard Megna/Fundamental Photographs; **38** Matt Meadows; **39** Maximilian Stock Ltd./Animals Animals; **40** Bob Daemmrich/Stock Boston; **41** Fundamental Photographs; **42** Color-Pic, Inc.; **44** Michael Newman/PhotoEdit; **45** (l)Tom Pantages, (r)Tom Pantages; **46** Jim Roshan/Roshan FOTO; **47** Alan Fortune/Earth Scenes; **48** John Lei/Stock Boston; **49** Tom Pantages; **50** Robert Lubeck/Earth Scenes; **51** Photo Researchers; **52** Richard Kolar/Earth Scenes; **53** Tom Pantages; **54** (l)Jeff Greenberg/PhotoEdit, (r)Chris Everard/Stone; **55** David Hall/Photo Researchers; **56** Tom Pantages; **57** Richard Hutchings/PhotoEdit; **58** (t)David Young-Wolff/PhotoEdit, (b)Tom Pantages; **59** John M. Roberts/The Stock Market; **60** Charles D. Winters/Charles D. Winters; **61** Chris Marona/Photo Researchers; **62** Jonathan Daniel/AllSport USA; **63** (tl)Craig van der Lende/Image Bank, (b)Corbis; **64** AP/Wide World Photos; **65** (l)Michael Dalton/Fundamental Photographs, (r)Michael Dalton/Fundamental Photographs; **66** Corbis; **67** Stock Boston; **69** Tom Pantages; **70** (t)Kevin Fleming/Corbis, (b)Myrleen Ferguson Cate/PhotoEdit; **71** Bill Aron/PhotoEdit; **72** Michael Newman/PhotoEdit/PictureQuest (PNI); **73** Elena Rooraid/PhotoEdit; **74** Stephen R. Swinburne/Stock Boston; **75** Felicia Martinez/PhotoEdit; **76** Bob Daemmrich/Stock Boston; **77** Tom Prettyman/PhotoEdit; **78** Photo Researchers; **79** Visuals Unlimited; **80** Stock Boston; **81** Michael Newman/PhotoEdit; **82** John Sohlder/Visuals Unlimited; **84** David Young-Wolff/PhotoEdit; **85** Lowell Georgia/Photo Researchers; **86** (t)Tony Freeman/PhotoEdit, (c)David Young-Wolff/PhotoEdit, (bl)Michael Newman/PhotoEdit, (br)Bonnie Kamin/PhotoEdit; **87** Mary Kate Denny/PhotoEdit; **88** Stephen Frisch/Stock Boston; **89** (tl)Tom Pantages, (cr)Felicia Martinez/PhotoEdit, (bl)Felicia Martinez/PhotoEdit, (br)Michael Newman/PhotoEdit; **90** (tl)Stuart McClymont/Stone, (cl)Tom Pantages, (tr)Michael Newman/PhotoEdit, (b)Michael Newman/PhotoEdit; **91** (tl)Michael Newman/PhotoEdit, (bl)Tom McHugh/Photo Researchers, (r)Lynn Stone/Animals Animals; **92** (tl)Felicia Martinez/PhotoEdit, (tr)Michael P. Gadomski/Photo Researchers, (b)Michael Newman/PhotoEdit; **93** (t)Felicia Martinez/PhotoEdit, (b)Phil Degginger/Color-Pic, Inc.; **94** Simon Fraser/Science Photo Library/Photo Researchers; **95** John J. Dommers/Photo Researchers; **96** David Joel/Stone; **97** Joe Cornish/Stone; **98** Kathleen Kliskey-Geraghty/Index Stock Imagery; **99** (l)Photo Researchers, (r)NASA/Photo Researchers; **100** Roger Ressmeyer/Corbis; **101** R. Packwood/Earth Scenes; **102** (tl)Photo Researchers, (bl)Photo Researchers, (r)Photo Researchers; **103** Jacques Jangoux/Stone; **104** James Marshall/Corbis.